ABOUT THE AUTHOR

Professor P. Henry van Laer was born in 1906 in the Netherlands. From 1923 to 1938 he studied philosophy, theology, mathematics, physical science and astronomy at various colleges and the State University of Leyden, from which he graduated in 1938 with the degree of Doctor of Science. In the scientific world he is known especially because of his research on caloric properties in superconductors. Most of this research was done in collaboration with Prof. Keesom, the world-famous specialist in the realm of extremely low temperatures. In 1946 he was appointed Professor of Philosophy at the University of Leyden. He is the author of six books and scores of articles on physical science, astronomy, and philosophico-scientific questions. In 1953 he taught at Duquesne University as Visiting Professor of the Philosophy of Nature and of Science.

PHILOSOPHY OF SCIENCE

Part One

SCIENCE IN GENERAL

DUQUESNE STUDIES

Philosophical Series

6

PHILOSOPHY OF SCIENCE

by

P. Henry van Laer, D.Sc.

PART ONE

SCIENCE IN GENERAL

AN INTRODUCTION TO SOME GENERAL
ASPECTS OF SCIENCE

SECOND EDITION

1963
DUQUESNE UNIVERSITY PRESS
Pittsburgh 19, Pa.
Editions E. Nauwelaerts, Louvain

DUQUESNE STUDIES

Philosophical Series

Andrew G. van Melsen, D.Sc., D.Ed., and Henry J. Koren, C.S.Sp., S.T.D., editors.

Library of Congress Catalog Card Number 63—11605

Volume Eleven—*Remy C. Kwant,* ENCOUNTER. Pp. VIII and 85. Price: cloth $3.25. Published also in Dutch.

Volume Twelve—*William A. Luijpen,* EXISTENTIAL PHENOMEN-OLOGY. Pp. XIII and 355. Second impression. Price: paper $6.00, cloth $6.75. Published also in Dutch.

Volume Thirteen—*Andrew G. van Melsen,* SCIENCE AND TECH-NOLOGY. Pp. X and 373. Price: paper $6.20, cloth $6.95. Published also in Dutch.

Volume Fourteen—*P. Henry van Laer,* PHILOSOPHY OF SCIENCE. Part Two: A STUDY OF THE DIVISION AND NATURE OF VARIOUS GROUPS OF SCIENCES. Pp. XIII and 342. Price: paper $5.75, cloth, $6.50.

Volume Fifteen — *Remy C. Kwant,* THE PHENOMENOLOGICAL PHILOSOPHY OF MERLEAU-PONTY. Pp. VIII and 257. Price: paper $4.50, cloth $5.25.

IN PREPARATION:

John Peters—METAPHYSICS
M. G. Plattel—SOCIAL PHILOSOPHY
Joseph A. Kockelmans—PHENOMENOLOGY AND PHYSICAL SCIENCE

OTHER SERIES OF DUQUESNE STUDIES:

Philological Series (three volumes to date)

Psychological Series (one volume to date)

Spiritan Series (six volumes to date)

Theological Series (one volume to date)

PERIODICALS PUBLISHED BY DUQUESNE UNIVERSITY PRESS:

Annuale Mediaevale. $4.00 per year.

Duquesne Hispanic Review. $3.00 per year.

Duquesne Review. A Journal of the Social Sciences. $2.25 per year.

Duquesne Science Counselor. $3.00 per year (foreign $3.25).

Review of Existential Psychology and Psychiatry. $5.00 per year.

CONTENTS

———

PREFACE

This book has grown from lectures I have delivered several times at the State University of Leyden and in the Spring of 1953 as visiting professor at Duquesne University, Pittsburgh. I have undertaken the burden of preparing the manuscript, because it became clear to me that my audience as well as others were sincerely interested in its contents, but especially because to the best of my knowledge there are very few books in which the problems considered in this study are given any extensive consideration. Whatever hesitation remained in me was overcome under the gentle prodding of the editor of DUQUESNE STUDIES.

This book will appear in two volumes. The first, which is the present volume, considers science in general, while the second, which is in preparation, will be concerned with the problem of the division of the sciences and the proper nature of the various groups of sciences.

In preparing the definite text and making the manuscript ready for the press I have been greatly assisted by Fr. Henry J. Koren, C.S.Sp., Professor at Duquesne University, who has contributed already so much to the publication of the other works that have appeared in this series. With respect to this volume he fully deserves the title of collaborator. Not only has he taken care of the definite English text, adapting and completing its contents wherever necessary according as needed by the English-speaking reader, but in addition his pertinent remarks have been a valuable contribution to the writing of this book. For this collaboration and especially for his unfailing friendly readiness to be of service I wish to offer him here my wholehearted thanks. However, the whole responsibility for the contents of this work is mine.

It is my sincere hope that this book will really fill a need and receive the same favorable reception as my previous publication in this series.

Leyden, December 1955

> DR. P. HENRY VAN LAER
> Professor at the State University of
> Leyden (Netherlands)

PREFACE TO THE SECOND EDITION

The first edition of this work was so well received that now, a few years after its publication, a reprint appears to be necessary to satisfy the continuing demand. This reception as well as most of the reviews in learned periodicals, which expressed praise and high regard for its content, were a source of satisfaction for its author. Several reviewers, however, also mentioned objections to certain parts of the work and formulated suggestions for its improvement. Unfortunately, economical and technical reasons prevent me from making substantial changes and additions in the text. For this reason I want to defend here the standpoint from which this book has been written insofar as this standpoint itself was criticized.

A few reviewers complained that the scope of the book was too traditional and that too little attention was paid to new conceptions and theories, such as logical empiricism, logistics, and statistical considerations. My reply to this objection is: I wanted to show that even in our time the classical problems of the theory of science continue to deserve full attention; therefore there is every reason to present a careful study of them. The fact that certain contemporary authors sometimes consider these problems to be no longer of any importance, gave us an added reason to insist on these classical issues.

Other reviewers regarded with disfavor the brevity with which certain topics, such as the object and the foundation of the sciences, were treated. I would have agreed with their criticism if this book had been presented as complete in itself. However, as its subtitle indicated, it was only the first part of a larger study, and this first part was devoted only to the most general aspects of the sciences. The second part was intended to offer an opportunity to speak more extensively about various problems within the framework of the various distinct groups of sciences. Meanwhile this second part has been published and, I hope, will have offered these reviewers most of the discussions which they vainly looked for in the first part.

I take this opportunity to express my gratitude to the Reverend Henry J. Koren, C.S.Sp., of Duquesne University, for his aid in preparing this second edition.

Leyden, January 1963

P. Henry van Laer

GENERAL INTRODUCTION

The Title of this Book. The title of this book PHILOSOPHY OF SCIENCE and the subtitle of the first volume SCIENCE IN GENERAL may give rise to misunderstanding unless some explanation is added because of the ambiguity of the terms, especially that of the term 'science', which is used in many senses. It is impossible to define exactly in a few words what is meant by these terms in this book. Any definition would require new explanations because of the ambiguity or analogy of the terms used to clarify matters. I will therefore abstain from any effort to explain in this introduction the exact meaning attributed to the terms used in the title. For that matter, the extensive table of contents preceding these pages is sufficient to give the interested reader a satisfactory idea concerning the subject matter treated in this work. I will therefore restrict myself in this introduction to a few brief remarks to indicate the main lines followed in this study and to prevent certain misunderstandings that could easily arise.

In the first place, I want to point out that the term 'science' is not restricted here to the physical sciences, as is usually done in English and French scientific literature, but is used in a very broad sense—namely, for science in general as well as each and any special science, no matter what its nature be, including theology and philosophy. If in particular chapters restrictions are made in the use of the term, this will always be justified and wherever possible indicated by the addition of a qualifying noun. Although the term 'science' is used in a very broad sense, a large number of the examples illustrating the text will be borrowed from the physical sciences. The reason is, first of all, that because of his former studies the author is most familiar with this domain, but also that the physical sciences often reveal most clearly the typical features of science.

Division of this Study. As every branch of philosophy, the philosophy of the sciences must devote itself to the more profound problems that arise in the realms of the sciences in question—problems therefore that cannot be considered within the domain of a definite specialized science. The philosophy of science is concerned, first of all, with the phenomenon of 'science' in general. It asks what is meant by 'to know' and 'science'. Next, it devotes itself to certain general characteristics of the sciences, such as abstraction and necessity, general considerations regarding the object and foundation of a science, the study of general scientific methods, and the critique of the value and importance of scientific hypotheses and theories. These and other similar problems will be discussed in the first volume of this work under the title SCIENCE IN GENERAL.

In the second volume, whose title is A STUDY OF THE DIVISION AND NATURE OF VARIOUS GROUPS OF SCIENCES, we will devote our attention to a consideration of important groups of sciences, such as theoretical and practical sciences, ideal and experiential sciences, natural and cultural sciences. Such groups of sciences will be studied according to their character, object, structure, limitation, method, etc.

Relation to Epistemology and Logic. Accordingly, the philosophy of science, as it is conceived here, is not a philosophy of knowledge or epistemology. Epistemology is primarily concerned with the problem of man's knowledge; the difference between sense cognition and intellectual cognition; the objective value of human knowledge; and the philosophical views of this value, such as realism, idealism, empiricism, etc. Thus the object of the philosophy of science, in the sense in which the term is used here, differs from that of the philosophy of knowledge. Of course, this does not preclude that occasionally questions or conclusions of the philosophy of knowledge will enter into our discussions, for by its very nature the philosophy of science is intimately connected with the philosophy of knowledge—so intimately even that several problems treated in this book are considered by others in connection with the philosophy of knowledge.

Sometimes also, part of the subject matter dealt with here is studied in more extensive treatises of logic. This is not surprising when it is taken into consideration that logic is the philosophical discipline which provides the norms of human thought and devotes itself especially to the way man's thoughts proceed from the known to the unknown. Accordingly, a major study of logic will formulate also general directives to be followed in scientific work. Thus with respect to a major part of its contents the philosophy of science may be considered as a continuation and extension of logic. Nevertheless, as will become clear in the reading of this book, the majority of the problems discussed here are given only scant attention, or even none at all, in the standard works on logic.

Remarks Concerning the Way of Treating the Subject Matter. Throughout the work we have assumed the realistic viewpoint, which in our opinion is the only one that can be philosophically justified. This viewpoint implies that we accept the existence of a real world independently of our thought, and that our cognitive powers supply us with a trustworthy, although analogous, picture of this world. Deviating views regarding the nature of human knowledge will be mentioned occasionally when for special reasons it seems to be useful; e.g., in the study of scientific induction and the chapter concerning hypothesis and theory.

In general, no attention, or almost none, is paid in this work to the subjective elements that enter into the study of science, the psychology of the man of research, the influence of all kinds of ideologies, the responsibility of the scientist with respect to the practical application of his scientific discoveries, and other similar questions. Moreover, the author was compelled to restrict himself both in the development of the problems considered and the choice of these problems, because otherwise this work would have become too voluminous. It is not to be expected that the actual choice of problems and the way they are treated will please every reader. Quite a few perhaps will look in vain for subjects in which they are especially interested, while attaching no importance to certain problems considered here. Likewise, the method followed will certainly not meet everyone's approval. There is no escape from this. Nevertheless, an author must have the liberty to select his problems and method in accordance with his own sphere of interest and his view of existing needs. For this reason I trust that, notwithstanding all its deficiencies and shortcomings, this book will receive a kind welcome.

References. It goes without saying that this study is not original in all respects. Every book has its own pre-history. As soon as one's interest is aroused in a definite subject or a number of specific problems, one will try to arrive at a more profound understanding by studying already existing works. Elements whose origin may be remembered or have been forgotten are assimilated with one's own views and integrated into the results of one's own reflection. Thus it will often be no longer possible to express by means of references to what extent one has depended on others. Nevertheless, I have tried as much as possible to indicate where I have made use of other publications. However, I want to make special mention here of a few books which have been a great aid to me in the first preparation of my lectures in the philosophy of science. They are the following: Dr. J. T. Beysens, LOGICA OF DENKLEER, Wassenaar, 1923; Dr. J. H. E. J. Hoogveld, INLEIDING TOT DE WIJSBEGEERTE, vol. I, revised by Dr. F. Sassen, Utrecht-Nijmegen, ⁴1947.

SCIENCE IN GENERAL

CHAPTER ONE

THE VARIOUS MEANINGS OF THE TERM 'SCIENCE'

1. *The Terms 'Science' and 'To Know'*

The Term 'Science'. The English term 'science' corresponds to the Latin *scientia,* which is derived from the verb *scire,* to know. Contrary to what is the case in Greek, Latin, and many modern languages with respect to the corresponding terms, in English there is no etymological connection between 'science' and 'to know'.[1] Nevertheless, one should keep in mind that there is an objective connection between the contents of the terms 'science' and 'to know', for all science consists in knowing, although not every form of knowing can qualify as science. Both terms too are analogous, i.e. both are used to express meanings which are partly the same and partly different.

The Meaning of 'To Know'. In general, one may say that 'to know', both in the sense of the French *savoir* (German *wissen,* Dutch *weten*) and in that of *connaître* (*kennen*), is an activity of living beings endowed with an intellect and/or senses, by means of which they are capable of representing the extra-mental world in themselves. A knowing being is a being which is able to have in itself the presence of some other thing precisely insofar as it is another thing. According as this presence terminates on the level of the senses or that of the intellect we distinguish two modes of knowledge: sensitive

---

[1]Greek *epistêmê* and *epistamai;* Latin *scientia* and *scire;* German *Wissenschaft* and *wissen;* Dutch *wetenschap* and *weten.* It is to be noted also that in many languages there are two verbs corresponding to the English verb 'to know': Greek *epistamai* and *gignôskô;* Latin *scire* and *novisse;* French *savoir* and *connaître;* German *wissen* and *kennen;* Dutch *weten* en *kennen;* Italian *sapere* and *conoscere;* Spanish *saber* and *conocer.* There is a difference in meaning between these two verbs. *Connaître, kennen,* etc. generally are used to indicate sense cognition, and intellectual cognition only if there is question of knowledge of concrete objects. *Savoir, wissen,* etc., on the other hand, are used to indicate intellectual knowledge with insight; they may be extended to sense knowledge if in this sense knowledge one considers an aspect that has a certain analogous resemblance to man's knowledge with intellectual insight; for instance, the French will say that a bird *'sait'* how to build its nest.

1

knowledge and intellectual knowledge. Irrational animals are endowed with only the first mode of knowing, whereas man is capable of knowing in both ways.[2]

2. *Sensitive and Intellectual Knowledge*

Sensitive Knowledge. In both man and animal there are various faculties of sensitive or sensorial knowledge. Usually five external senses are enumerated: sight, hearing, taste, smell, and touch. In addition, it is traditional to distinguish four internal senses: the central sense or common sensitivity, imagination, sense memory, and the estimative sense. By means of these various faculties of sensitive knowledge an animal knows its food, surroundings, the suitability of certain materials for building its nest, etc. Man also knows in a sensitive way; e.g. extra-mental reality as to its sense-perceptible aspects, his internal sensations, imaginations, etc.

In general, we may say that sensitive knowledge is concerned with things in their individual concreteness: this particular tree or that particular house with those determinate sense-perceptible qualities is reached. The knowledge obtained by means of the senses finds its culminating point on the sensitive level in an image produced by the imagination, the so-called *phantasm.*

Intellectual Knowledge. All intellectual knowledge is commonly referred to a single supra-sensitive faculty of knowledge, called the intellect, which is not found below the level of man. It is by means of this faculty that man reaches extra-mental reality on the abstract or universal level. No longer is knowledge limited to particular objects in their concreteness, but the intellect rises above concrete individuality and seizes the common nature which lies concealed, as it were, below its extra-mental realizations. The nature seized in this operation of the intellect is expressed in an intellectual image, called an *idea* or *concept,* which forms the terminus of the first operation of the human mind. The action by which the intellect joins or divides the contents of two concepts as subject and predicate is called a *judgment;* e.g., water is a liquid, bodies attract one another. The

---

[2]It is beyond the scope of this study to enter into details about the nature of knowledge. The interested reader may be referred to *ex professo* treatises of rational psychology, philosophical anthropology, and epistemology, such as George P. Klubertanz, *The Philosophy of Human Nature,* New York, 1953; Henry J. Koren, *The Philosophy of Animate Nature,* St. Louis, 1955; Fernand Van Steenberghen, *Epistemology,* New York, 1949.

process by which the intellect derives a new proposition from two other propositions which have one common term is called an act of *reasoning*.

3. Scientific Knowledge

Its Requirements. It is obvious that not just any kind of knowledge may be called scientific. To deserve this name, knowledge must meet certain requirements. They are the following:

1) It must be on the *intellectual* level. This requirement is so elementary that any comment would seem to be belaboring the obvious. No matter how often a sensation is repeated, no matter how many objects are reached by the senses, sense-perception remains an experience of the individual in all its concreteness. Hence the limitations inherent in sensitive knowledge as such preclude it from ever reaching the level of universality implied by scientific knowledge.

2) It must be *certain*, at least if certainty is possible with respect to the object considered by the knower. If certainty cannot be obtained, one has to be satisfied, at least provisionally, with knowledge that is merely *probable*.

3) It must give an *insight into the causes* of the object under consideration. Hence in order to be scientific, knowledge may not be limited to mere facts, but must embrace also the foundations and causes which account for the facts. The ideal would be to know not merely the causes themselves, but to have knowledge of the causes *qua* causes, i.e. to have an insight into the working of the causes in question. In many cases we know the factor or factors which must be considered to be active in a process and therefore its cause or causes in the ordinary sense of the term; yet we do not have an insight into the causal influence as such. For example, we know that somehow the mass of the earth 'causes' bodies to be attracted by it, but we do not know exactly how mass causes this effect.

Such a knowledge with insight into the causes certainly was the ideal Aristotle had in mind in his *Posterior Analytics*:

> We suppose ourselves to possess unqualified *scientific knowledge* of a thing, as opposed to knowing it in the accidental way in which the sophist knows, when we think that we know the cause

on which the fact depends, as the cause of that fact and of no other, and further, that the fact *could not be other than it is*[3]

Various Opinions Concerning Knowledge and Science. The terms 'knowledge' and 'science' may be given different meanings in accordance with one's general philosophic views concerning the value, nature, scope, and limits of human knowledge. A proposition such as 'metals expand when heated', no matter how simple and clear its meaning may seem to be, has an entirely different meaning according as one is a realist, an empiricist, a Kantian or a neo-positivist.[4] However, fascinating as the study of these various meanings may be, it is beyond the scope of our present discussion to enter into any details. Our own viewpoint is that of the realism which underlies Aristotelian-Thomistic philosophy. This viewpoint has at its disposal an impressive array of arguments for which, however, we must refer the reader to *ex professo* treatises of the matter.[5]

4. *The Various Meanings of 'Science' and 'Scientific'*

'Science' and 'scientific' are terms which may be used in an analogous sense to express various meanings.

1. In a *subjective* sense the term 'science' is used to indicate:

a. The *actual operation* of the human intellect by means of which at a given moment man understands or 'knows' a particular state of affairs in its foundation; in other words, by which one here and now has a particular scientific insight, for instance, into a mathematical theorem, a physical or a historical problem. Accordingly, what is meant here is, as the ancients called it, *'scientia qua scitur'*, 'science by means of which something is known'.

b. The *habitual knowledge* one has concerning a group of problems or a definite realm of the data of experience, and the *habitual ability* to handle scientific problems of a certain kind. In this sense one may possess the science of chemistry, mathematics, or economics. In a still broader sense we speak of a 'man of science' or a 'scientific

---

[3]*Post. Anal.* I, 2; 71b 9-12. Translation of the W. D. Ross edition of *The Works of Aristotle Translated Into English.* Quoted with permission of the Oxford University Press.
[4]Cf. Andrew G. Van Melsen, *From Atomos to Atom* (*Duquesne Studies, Philosophical Series,* vol. 1), Pittsburgh, 1952, pp. 169ff.
[5]Cf. for instance, Fernand Van Steenberghen, *Epistemology,* New York, 1949.

mind' with respect to one who enjoys the intellectual ability to handle scientific problems in general.

2. In an *objective* sense the terms 'science' and 'scientific' are used to indicate that which is the object of 'science in the subjective sense'. In other words, they indicate that which is grasped actually or habitually by intellectual cognition and is, as it were, present in man's mind and ready for further use. The ancients called this *'scientia quae scitur'*, 'science which is known'. This is the meaning of 'science' in such sentences as 'in this point his science is weak, but in that point it is strong' and 'his science does not go that far'.

3. The term 'science' is used also to indicate the whole of cognitive activities, both intellectual and sensitive, by means of which man is able to acquire knowledge of himself and his surrounding world. In this sense the term is more or less synonymous with the *study of science*. Taken in this way, 'science' may be placed alongside or in contrast with other terms indicating other spheres of human activity; e.g. faith and science, science and art, science and technique. This is the meaning of the term 'science' also in sentences such as 'science is bound by the requirements of its objects and the human mind'; 'science must obey the laws of logic and its own inner law'; 'science has its limits'; 'there is a certain amount of fashion in science'; 'science has revealed many of the world's secrets'; 'science leads to God'; 'to promote science'.

4. 'Science' is used also as a collective noun indicating the whole body of *men devoted to science*. In this sense the term occurs, for instance, in the following sentences: 'science needs freedom'; 'science has a great responsibility or a definite task with respect to society'; 'science must be objective and unprejudiced'.

5. Very often the term 'science' is used to indicate a particular realm of human knowledge which shows a certain inner connection and can be distinguished from other similar realms by means of its proper characteristics. In this case the term indicates at the same time a particular *system* of interconnected theses in a specific realm of knowledge which is the result of the study of science (science in the third sense) in a particular sphere. When this meaning is given to the term, it is possible to use it in the plural; for instance, mathe-

matical sciences, experiential sciences, physical sciences. This sense of 'science' will be considered more in detail in Chapter Two.

6. Finally, the terms 'science' and 'scientific' may be used with respect to something that in one way or the other is simply *connected* with science in any of the above-enumerated senses. For instance, a 'scientific' book or a 'scientific' treatise is a book concerned with science in the fifth sense; a 'scientific' attitude is an attitude proper to science in the third sense; also expressions such as 'scientific instruments', a 'science building', or 'scientific management'.

Remark. It may be useful to add here that the various above-mentioned meanings of science are all very closely related, so that the meaning intended in a given context can possibly be classified under more than one heading. Moreover, as will be emphasized more in detail in Chapter Two, one must never lose sight of the fact that in all its meanings the term 'science' implies a certain relation to man's cognitive activity. 'Science' and 'scientific' are concepts which always refer, at least implicitly, to man and the specifically human activity of intellectual cognition.

CHAPTER TWO

SCIENCE AS A SYSTEM

Introduction

The purpose of this chapter is to investigate the important characteristics of 'science as a system' in order to acquire an understanding of the structure of a science and thus to arrive at a suitable description or definition of this concept. Accordingly, when we speak here of science, we take the term in the sense given to it in no. 5 of the preceding section.

The Human Character of Science. When science is taken in this sense, one thinks of the results of man's study of science in a particular realm, results which as an interconnected whole of theses can be written down and possibly assembled into a book. Thus science, considered in this sense, would be able to have an objective existence outside man. Although in subsequent pages such a view of science is not likely to cause difficulties, nevertheless it is good always to keep in mind that such an imaginary existence of science outside man possesses hardly any meaning. Just as science in any of the other senses, so also science as a system is by its very nature unthinkable without its relationship to man. On the one hand, it is the result of human thinking; on the other, it has meaning only insofar as in the written or spoken language it can again become the spiritual possession of human beings, who in their own way assimilate and perhaps develop or modify the results others have obtained before them. Thus science as a system is not at all something rigid or static, but on the contrary it is a dynamic whole which is born and grows, is subject to all kinds of changes, and is developed in scope and depth in and through the intellectual activity of human beings. Taken in this sense, therefore, science is never something purely objective, but, as it exists in reality, i.e. as it is possessed by man, it is always a web of subjectivity and objectivity.

When there is question here of the *structure* of science, we mean the internal composition, given to it by human activity, which, on the one hand, is determined by the nature of the object studied and, on the other, by the way in which man is able to grasp this object intellectually.

7

This important remark concerning the human character of science should be kept in mind, for in the further development of our study this human aspect will not be all the time emphasized again, so that perhaps one will get the impression that we have not paid sufficient attention to it.

Starting Point. In the study of science as a system our starting point will be taken from the provisional knowledge of science possessed by anyone who is at least to a certain extent at home in the world of science. Such a person will know that there exist a number of sciences and that they differ in characteristics and importance. For example, as sciences may be considered theology, philosophy, physical science, astronomy, economics, ethnology, philology, psychology, biology, etc. We speak of positive and exact sciences, experiential sciences, physical and cultural sciences. Hence the question arises as to what is common to all these sciences. What is the basis which allows us to indicate all these systems and many others by the common term 'science'? What are the characteristic traits which can be found in each and every science, the conditions which must be fulfilled before one can speak of 'science'? In the following pages we will attempt to consider these characteristics and conditions in a number of brief remarks (1-7). It will become clear that some of the required characteristics are more concerned with the form of a science (1, 3, 6, 7) and others with its contents (2, 4, 5).

1. *Science Is a System*

It is clear that any knowledge to which the name 'science' is given must show a certain coherence. It must constitute a coherent whole of interconnected things and their parts that is appropriately ordered. An enumeration of unrelated facts or data, no matter how much each of them be worth knowing, does not give rise to a science. Later, in nos. 6 and 7, we will determine more exactly in what this systematic character consists and how it arises.

Although this point is fairly obvious, nevertheless it needs to be stressed. Nowadays people are frequently held to be 'scientific' and 'intellectual' if they are in possession of a large amount of information about almost any subject under the sun, even if they have not the slightest idea at all regarding the interrelationship of the things known. I cannot resist quoting here the warning sounded by Newman in the nineteenth century in his book THE IDEA OF A UNIVERSITY. "An intellectual man, as the world now conceives of him, is one who is full of "views" on all subjects of philosophy, on all matters of the day. It is almost thought a disgrace not to have a view at a moment's notice on any question from the Personal Advent to the Cholera or Mesmerism. This is owing in great measure to the necessities of periodical literature, now so much in request. Every quarter of a year, every month, every day, there must be a supply, for the gratification of the public, of new and luminous theories, on the subjects of religion, foreign politics, home politics, civil economy, finance, trade, agriculture, emigration, and the colonies. Slavery, the gold fields, German philosophy, the French Empire, Wellington, Peel, Ireland, must be practised on, day after day, by what are called original thinkers. As the great man's guest must produce his good stories or songs at the evening banquet, as the platform orator exhibits his telling facts at mid-day, so the journalist lies under the stern obligation of extemporizing his lucid views, leading ideas, and nut-shell truths for the breakfast table. The very nature of periodical literature, broken into small wholes, and demanded punctually to an hour, involves the habit of this extempore philosophy."[1]

According to Newman, true science must be a make-weight against the popular journalistic pseudo-knowledge which comes from news-papers, Sunday magazines, book reviews, etc. If he were alive today, he would undoubtedly add the radio, movies, and television.[2]

2. *A Science is Concerned with a Definite Field of Knowledge*

Notwithstanding all its capacities, the human intellect is not able to take hold of all knowable things under all possible aspects. In former ages it was possible for a few outstanding intellects, such as those of Aristotle and Albert the Great, to dominate the whole of con-temporary science. It was possible to call a man like Albert the Great the 'Universal Doctor' and a contemporary could say of him: "Thou knowest whatever can be known", "*totum scibile scisti*". Yet, even in those times, certain branches of learning were clearly marked off as autonomous or quasi-autonomous realms of knowledge. At an early date mathematics and astronomy, for example, were considered as separate sciences because of the characteristic nature of their object

---

[1]*Preface.* In the Longmans, Green & Co. ed. of 1947, pp. xxxvi f.
[2]Cf. Charles F. Harrold in his *Introduction* to the above-quoted edition of Newman's work, p. xx.

and methods. According as in the course of time the total of ac-
cumulated knowledge increased, and the development of technique
offered new means of scientific investigation, it became increasingly
clear that it was necessary to divide the immense realm open to
scientific knowledge into definite fields, each of which gave rise to
a special science. Regarding the methods which govern the demarca-
tion of these definite fields of knowledge, they will be mentioned
in the chapter concerning the object of the sciences (Ch. V).

3. *Science is Preferably Expressed in Universal Statements*

A mere description of the subject matter observed and studied
does not constitute a science. Likewise, a mere enumeration of the
problems which arise in a particular field of knowledge does not
amount to a science. For in both cases there is no manifestation of
insight into the subject matter, which is required in any science. So
efforts must be made to arrive at conclusions that are based upon an
intellectual understanding and expressed in statements of the type
'so it is' or 'so it ought to be'.

In general, every science tries to acquire an insight into the
specific nature of things, their specific properties or activities, and also
the essential interconnection of phenomena according to their specific
character. Thus the individual as such does not lie in the center of
scientific interest, but only the individual insofar as it can be considered to represent the specific. For instance, the physicist is not
interested in this particular source of light or that particular magnet,
this individual sample of water or helium, but in the properties of
light, magnets, water or helium which he wants to define in universally
valid statements. The process by which the universal is abstracted
from the individual does not concern us here immediately, but will
be discussed in Chapter Three.

Nevertheless, it may happen sometimes that science is interested
in individual and concrete objects or events; e.g. in astronomy, when
the sun, the moon, particular planets, or other celestial bodies are studied; in geology, when the earth is considered with respect to its
actual appearance as a whole and in its parts; and above all in history.
However, even in such cases what matters is usually not the individual
as such. Otherwise this type of knowledge would hardly rise above
sense cognition. On the contrary, even in these cases an effort is made
to discover universal aspects in the individual phenomenon or to ex-

plain the individual as a concrete form of general or specific essences whose nature is laid down in universal propositions.

Thus we see that it belongs to the essence of science that the results are expressed in *universal* statements, i.e. laws or rules expressing that a definite species or genus is like this or ought to be like this. Of course, the principles also upon which a science is built—which may be borrowed from another science—are expressed in general propositions. The predicate of such general propositions, whether they serve as the starting point or formulate the result of the science in question, can be applied to the subordinates of the subject in a distributive way. This makes it possible to apply the knowledge obtained to new particular cases in a deductive way (Cf. Ch. VII, sect. I, no. 2).

4. *The Statements of Science Must be True or Probably True*

The statements resulting from scientific research must be true and certain, at least if truth and certainty are within the reach of man with respect to the problem under consideration. It is to be noted that truth and certainty are not the same. A statement is *true* if *objectively* it is in conformity with reality, i.e. if it expresses the nature of things as they are independently of the consideration of the mind. A statement is called *certain* or *probable* for *subjective* reasons, i.e. according as the mind adheres to the statement firmly, without any fear of error, or with a certain fear of being mistaken. With respect to the truth of a particular proposition, the mind can pass through a whole series of states, from a mere conjecture or suspicion through a more or less firmly held opinion to absolute certainty. Although in general a proposition will be true if we are subjectively certain of it, a subjective state of certainty with respect to a proposition that is objectively false is possible. In such a case we have to do with *false certainty*.[3]

With respect to scientific statements, the ideal is that they be true. If in a particular case this ideal is not within reach, then the statements will have to be at least probably true. Moreover, in the case of true statements we must be certain of their truth.

---

[3]It is beyond the scope of this work to go into further details concerning the nature of truth, certainty, probability, etc. The interested reader may be referred to *ex professo* treatises of the matter, such as Van Steenberghen's above-quoted *Epistemology* or that of P. Coffey.

5. *Science is Concerned with the Essence, Foundation, Causes, and Finality of its Objects*

Not every system of universal statements regarding a definite field of knowledge constitutes a science. It is not sufficient that the statements express things which are, their actual qualities, and their mutual interrelations. All this is necessary, but only as the starting point of further study which will have to give us an intellectual understanding of the foundation of these qualities, the nature and reason of their interconnection, and the causes of the phenomena. The concept of cause will have to be taken in the broadest possible sense; hence it should not be restricted to efficient causes, but extended also to final, material, and formal causes. The last two kinds of causes constitute in their inseparable union the essence of material things, the 'formed matter', while the final cause reveals itself in the inner finality of reality. In other words, the statements resulting from authentic scientific research will have to refer to the efficient causes of the phenomena, the essence of the things considered and therefore the foundation of their properties and activities, and finally their inner finality, i.e. that aspect of their essence which gives us an insight into the coordination of the component parts into one common result.

Because the statements of science refer to the specific or generic essences of things, a certain necessity will be implied in the expressed relationship of subject and predicate. The contingent element in the data of experience is removed from the cognitive content by means of intellectual abstraction. This process of intellectual abstraction which gives the propositions their character of universality is at the same time the foundation of the necessity present in the connection between the subject and the predicate of the propositions. This necessity may be of a different nature in accordance with the subject matter to which it refers. We distinguish metaphysical, mathematical, physical, and moral necessity. This point will be considered more in detail in our study of abstraction (Ch. III, sect. II, no. 3) and necessity in science (Ch. IV).

Sometimes it is possible to grasp the essential in a given concrete cognitive content immediately by means of formal abstraction. This happens, for instance, frequently in mathematics and philosophy. In the experimental sciences, however, often complicated research, called scientific induction, is required to penetrate into the essential core.

We will return to this point in our discussion of scientific induction (Ch. VIII).

6. *The Statements of Science Must be Logically Ordered*

Although the very term 'system' more or less implies a logical order, nevertheless it is worth stressing that, as is commonly admitted by all, logical order is an essential requirement of science. The statements and conclusions concerning the essences and causes of the object in a definite field of knowledge may not be enumerated in an arbitrary way, but have to be arranged and classified according to a definite principle and following a definite method.

Thus we understand why Newman held very strongly that

> The first step in intellectual training is to impress upon a boy's mind the idea of science, method, order, principle, and system; of rule and exception, of richness and harmony.[4]

> Hence it is that critical scholarship is so important a discipline for him when he is leaving school for the University.[5]

Without critical training it is, indeed, impossible for anyone to do serious scientific work.

An essential element of science itself must be the methodical arrangement and classification of its statements, from the very starting point to the conclusions, in accordance with a logical order, such as that from the simple to the complicated, or from the known to the unknown. This order and classification are subject to variation according to the method chosen by the investigator with due attention for his purpose or the inner finality of science itself. Hence various methods of science can be distinguished, which are treated in the part of logic or philosophy that is called methodology. We will devote some consideration to them in the chapter concerning the methods of science (Ch. VII).

7. *Science Must Explain its Investigations and Arguments*

To the six conditions enumerated above one more has to be added. Not any logically ordered collection of universal and true statements in a definite field of knowledge concerning the essences and causes of things constitutes a science or a scientific work. Science, as it is gen-

---

[4] *Op. cit.,* p. xxxv.
[5] *Op. cit.,* p. xxxvi.

erally understood, requires that there be a connection between the statements, so as to make it possible to arrive at a judgment regarding their justification. Accordingly, we must require of a science that its problems and conclusions be connected by means of an explanation of the investigation, research, and especially the arguments and demonstrations that have led to its conclusions. The same is implied by St. Thomas when he describes science in the proper sense as knowledge acquired by means of demonstration.

8. *Descriptive Definition of Science*

According to the preceding considerations, in which we have made explicit what everyone accepts implicitly as the essential characteristics of science, we may now propose the following descriptive definition of science as a system:

Science is a logically ordered system of true, or at least probably true, and universal statements concerning the essences, foundations, causes and finality of objects in a definite field of knowledge, with reference to the investigations, arguments, and demonstrations upon which the conclusions are based.

9. *Further Division of the First Part of this Work*

In a science which fulfils the above-mentioned descriptive definition it is possible to distinguish several constitutive elements or aspects which, for the sake of a better understanding of the character and structure of a science, need to be developed more fully. They are the following:

1. An important element in the construction of a science is so-called *abstraction*. Because of the importance of this intellectual operation, a special chapter will be devoted to it (Chapter Three).

2. The statements of a science have a character of *necessity*. This necessity will be considered in Chapter Four.

3. Every science has a definite area of study which it considers from a definite point of view. Problems concerning this point will be discussed in Chapter Five, which deals with the *object* of science.

4. Every science is based upon certain *foundations*. It has a certain *starting point* and usually also certain *presuppositions*. They will be studied in Chapter Six.

5. The logical structure and character proper to sciences require that certain *methods* be followed. The most important of these scientific methods will be dealt with in Chapters Seven and Eight.

6. The entire procedure of a science aims at investigating the objects in its field according to their essences, foundations, and causes. In this investigation it will often be necessary to start from a *hypothesis* concerning the probable foundations and causes. This hypothesis will have to serve as a basis of a *theory* in which the consequences of the hypothesis are further developed. The formation of a hypothesis is usually guided by certain analogous resemblances of the unknown phenomena to other, known, phenomena. Hypothesis and theory, as well as the method of *analogy* leading to a hypothesis, will be the objects of our attention in Chapter Nine.

7. In one way or another, every science has to prove its conclusions. Therefore, a study of *demonstration* will be necessary (Chapter Ten).

The differences that can be observed with respect to some of these elements and aspects give rise to the possibility of characteristically different sciences. Hence they can provide an opportunity for a rational and reasonable division of the sciences, which will be discussed in the second part of this work. This is an additional reason why a more extensive study of these elements and aspects is justified.

CHAPTER THREE

ABSTRACTION IN SCIENCE

I. THE MEANING OF ABSTRACTION

The notion of abstraction is extensively discussed in the textbooks of logic, to which I could refer the reader here. However, it seems desirable to discuss at least those aspects of abstraction that are more important for the subject matter of this book, especially because they are often precisely the aspects which the textbooks consider only in a very sketchy way or not at all.

Negative and Positive Aspects of Abstraction. The terms 'abstraction' and 'to abstract' are analogous and therefore vary in meaning, although these various meanings are interconnected and partially have the same thought content. This common content has a twofold aspect, one of which is negative and the other positive. The positive aspect is *to abstract something,* i.e. to extract or draw forth something that is going to be considered. The negative aspect is *to abstract from something,* i.e. to leave out of consideration those elements in the data of the senses to which no attention is going to be paid. Accordingly, we must call abstract any intellectual operation which is not concerned with the whole content of a sense datum but only with one aspect of it and leaves out of consideration the other aspects or parts. Because of the very nature of our intellectual operations, such an abstraction of a cognitive object from the data of sense experience will often take place quite spontaneously; for instance, in the formation of intellectual concepts and that of many intellectual judgments.

Different Types of Abstraction. In epistemology and logic several kinds of abstraction are distinguished. This distinction, however, is not based upon a principle that gives rise to a clear-cut division, but rather upon the different character which the positive and negative aspects of an abstractive operation may have. Accordingly, the distinction of different types of abstraction often contains an element of suitability for a particular purpose which may vary from author to author. In consequence, one and the same kind of abstraction is sometimes indicated by different names, and this easily leads to mis-understandings.

Because of the scope of this study, I will restrict myself to a discussion of *total abstraction* (Section II), *formal* and *analytic* abstraction (Section III), and *simplifying* or *idealizing* abstraction (Section V).

II. TOTAL ABSTRACTION

1. *The Meaning of Total Abstraction*

The first type of abstraction, which plays an indispensable role in the formation of universal intellectual concepts from the data of sense experience, used to be called 'total abstraction' by the medieval scholastics. Generally it is this type that is meant when in philosophy and especially in logic there is question of abstraction without any further qualification.

Abstraction of the Specific Concept. All our knowledge, including that of science, takes its starting point in sense experience. But because of their materiality, the realities experienced, and therefore also the corresponding sense data, are individual and concrete and consequently incommunicable. The abstractive power of the intellect strips these particular data of their individuality and concreteness, i.e. of everything which belongs exclusively to this individual concrete thing in these concrete conditions (negative aspect of abstraction), while that which is common to individuals of the same kind is seized (positive aspect) and expressed in so-called 'abstract concepts', which then can be used as the predicate or the subject of a judgment. In this way the intellect obtains concepts which because of their abstract character no longer refer to the individual and concrete sense data from which they originated, but on the contrary have a universal character, i.e. are applicable to all individuals of the same kind. The result therefore of the total abstraction is the specific concept or logical *species*. Because of its universal character, this concept contains implicitly in itself as inferiors all the individuals which participate in the specific essence, and may be used as a predicate in a judgment of which the inferiors are the subject.

Abstraction of a Generic Concept. If in progressive abstraction the specific element also is left out, one will obtain a cognitive content that is still poorer, but therefore also wider in extension and applicability. It is called a generic concept or a logical *genus*. For instance, by means of an intellectual consideration of human individuals one obtains the concept 'man'; by further abstracting from the specifically human element one reaches the generic concept of 'sentient living being' or 'animal'; if next abstraction is made from the sensitive element, the result will be the concept of 'living being', which is also a generic concept but of a higher rank. In this way it is possible by means of progressive abstraction to form a series of concepts which steadily decrease in content but continually increase in extension or applicability; for instance the series man—sentient living being—living being—material thing.

No matter how far this abstraction is pushed, the result will always be a cognitive content which represents a logical whole (a *totum*), a group or class (a *species* or a *genus*) of things. For this reason we speak here of '*total* abstraction'. Because of the universal character of the concepts formed in this way also the term '*universal* abstraction' is used.

2. *Total Abstraction Does Not Falsify Reality*

Obviously, the content of an abstract concept represents reality only in an incomplete way—namely, insofar as the cognitive content does not contain the concrete individual particularities without which the thing does not exist. Nevertheless the concept may adequately represent the specific essence which is realized in a particular way in the individuals of that species, and in this way the abstract concept indicates the whole object. For instance, the specific concept 'man' or even the generic concept 'sentient living being' refers to the whole man as he exists concretely and individually, for there is nothing in the human individual that is not human or not sentient-living. Accordingly, a definition of 'man', which is applicable also to the individual human being, will always have to express the specific element and, either implicitly or explicitly, also the generic element; for instance, man is a sentient living being endowed with an intellect. Notwithstanding its abstract character, therefore, an abstract concept possesses a value for reality and does not falsify reality, although it is true that it does not adequately represent reality.

3. *Total Abstraction, Universality, and Necessity*

As we have seen above, it is total abstraction which by leaving aside the concrete and individual particularities lays the foundation for the universality of intellectual concepts and the possibility of the judgments of the intellect. Accordingly, by means of total abstraction, which gives thought a universal character, the possibility is given to arrive at the universal validity of scientific statements which was pointed out in the third section of Chapter Two.

All scientific knowledge is always expressed in propositions; first perhaps in singular propositions, when there is question of expressing a concrete event occurring in individual things, but then in universal propositions, which are concerned with the specific or generic element of things. In the elaboration of acquired knowledge use is made of deductive reasoning processes which consist in chains of judgments and are expressed in a number of propositions. Because a judgment or proposition in general is not conceivable without abstract concepts, at least insofar as the predicate is concerned, it will be manifest that without total abstraction no scientific activity would be possible.

Universality implies the character of necessity, which therefore is proper to a universal statement—namely, insofar as universality is an inseparable aspect of the specific essence that is formally seized by the intellect from the data of reality. Thus the necessity belonging to the proposition is founded on the essential relationship which the intellect discovers in the sense data by means of formal abstraction. In other words, the necessity of the judgment (logical aspect) is based upon the inner necessity of things (ontological aspect). The first is a consequence of total abstraction; the second follows from formal abstraction, which will be considered in the next section (especially no. 4).

4. *Total Abstraction and the Division of the Sciences*

As we have seen above, total abstraction admits degrees insofar as first abstraction is made from the concrete and individual, then from the specific, and finally, again in different degrees, from the generic. In this way a series of concepts arises whose content decreases steadily while its extension increases. Such a graded abstraction can be the basis of a subalternation or subordination of sciences or branches of a science according to their object. For instance, hydromechanics and the mechanics of solid bodies may be considered as subalternates of general mechanics; the theories of light and sound are subordinated to the general wave theory.

Remark. The above-mentioned subalternation of sciences is not the only one that is possible and certainly not the most important.

More important is the subalternation of sciences according to principles, i.e. if one science is based upon principles whose foundation
lies in another science. Moreover, one may speak of subalternation
when one science considers a secondary aspect of the object of another
science; for instance, animal ethology or the science of animal behavior is subordinated to general zoology. However, we will not
insist upon these subalternations.

III. FORMAL AND ANALYTIC ABSTRACTION

1. *The Meaning of Formal Abstraction*

Formal Abstraction in the Broad Sense of the Term. As a matter
of fact, any knowledge is an abstraction in the sense that not the
whole object known is assimilated by the knower but only the knowable form, the 'formal' elements, without matter. Only the formal
elements are capable of giving rise to a sensitive or intellectual image.
For this reason philosophers speak here of *formal abstraction.* This
kind of abstraction occurs in both sensitive and intellectual knowledge.
In sense cognition the sensible form is abstracted from the datum
of experience, and in intellectual cognition the intelligible form.
Thus the concept of 'abstraction', taken in the formal sense, has a
very wide range of application. Every sense formally abstracts a
determined kind of sensible qualities, but abstracts from the others;
the eye, for example, abstracts color and abstracts from sound, taste,
hardness, etc. The intellect also can formally abstract a definite aspect
of reality while abstracting from others. In considering a real object
a mathematical mind will look, for instance, for its spatial arrangement, universally valid formal properties, or quantitative relationships;
a philosopher of nature will consider separately, e.g. the spatial or
temporal aspects of material reality. There is formal abstraction also
when a psychologist, for example, pays attention only to the character or intellectual capacities of an individual and not to his external
appearance. Accordingly, in formal abstraction also the two above-
mentioned aspects occur—namely, the positive aspect that is formally
abstracted from the concrete datum, and the negative aspect insofar
as other 'sides' of a reality are left out of consideration.

Formal Abstraction in the Strict Sense of the Term. The formal
abstraction of the intellect, in the strict sense of the term, which is
usually meant when philosophers speak of formal abstraction, char-

acterizes the intellectual mode of knowing. As has been pointed out in the preceding section, our intellectual knowledge ultimately goes back to sense experience. But the data of sense experience as such are not suitable objects of the intellect, and the same must be said with respect to the images formed by the imagination. Precisely because of their materiality the essence of material things is veiled and concealed from us and therefore unknowable in this condition. This material character is retained, although in a different way, in the sense images that are formed by the material organs of the senses and the imagination. It is only through a process of dematerialization that they can become suitable objects of the immaterial intellect and be expressed in immaterial intellectual concepts. This dematerialization is the negative aspect of the intellectual operation that is called *formal abstraction*. The positive aspect consists in this that through this operation the intelligible essential form or another intelligible aspect of reality becomes the formal cognitive content of the intellect. Because this formal abstraction of the intellect in and through the process of dematerialization removes also the concrete and individual particularities of the object known, it is at the same time a total abstraction (cf. below, no. 6). Thus it happens that it is often possible to apply to concepts or cognitive contents obtained through formal abstraction the process of generalization, which we first met with in total abstraction and which consists in this that concepts can be arranged according to decreasing content and increasing extension; for instance, redness, color, visible quality, sense perceptible quality.

Remarks. Man's cognition is the activity of a single human being, although a sensitive and intellectual sphere can be distinguished in it; therefore, a conscious sense cognitive activity will always have a continuation on the intellectual level by means of a spontaneous abstractive operation that is both formal and total. In this way the intellect is capable of pronouncing a judgment on the actual cognitive object with respect to its whole essential form or a particular formal aspect. In general, it will not be possible to separate the considered elements or aspects of the reality in question completely from those that are left out of consideration. What is not explicitly considered will often be implicitly present in the total content of cognition.

When formal abstraction has the character of a direct intellectual vision of the object's essential aspects, as happens e.g. in the discovery of the first principles in the realm of philosophy and mathematics (cf. no. 4), the term *intuitive abstraction* or also *abstractive intui-*

tion can be used, the term 'intuition' being derived from the Latin *intueri*, to gaze at, to contemplate, to acquire insight.

2. *The Meaning of Analytic Abstraction*

A procedure in which the parts or aspects of a whole are considered separately and successively alongside one another amounts to an intellectual analysis of what is given in experience. If the emphasis is placed upon this analytic method of study, it is called also '*analytic* abstraction'. Such an analytic abstraction is essentially a formal abstraction—namely, insofar as one selects every time a particular aspect of a complex object. Nevertheless, in practice a difference is made between formal and analytic abstraction, and this in the following way.

a) The term 'analytic abstraction' is preferred when through successive formal considerations of the component parts or aspects of a whole one tries to obtain a more comprehensive view of this whole. For instance, in a green spherical object one may consider separately its green color, spherical shape, construction, elasticity, etc.; in a vibrating tuning-fork one may consider successively the vibration as a definite kind of motion, or as a source of sound, etc.

b) Preference is given to the term 'formal abstraction' when there is question of an intellectual abstraction accompanied by insight into the abstracted cognitive content; while, on the other hand, the term 'analytic abstraction' is preferably reserved for the abstractive operation in which the considered aspects lie more on the sensitive level, and intellectual insight into the foundation or value of these aspects is wholly or partially absent.

Its Use. Analytic abstraction is made use of in daily life as well as in science; e.g. in making classifications and especially in statistics. A group of objects may be classified differently according as a different aspect is considered. For instance, a group of students may be classified according to age, sex, religion, social background, type of studies, etc. Cases of cancer may be classified according to age, sex, social conditions, etc. of the patients or according to region, climate, soil conditions and similar factors. In this way it is possible to obtain statistical data that are useful for life and science. We will return to the question of analytic abstraction in Chapter Seven, where we will deal with complete induction.

3. *Formal Abstraction Does Not Falsify Reality*

Insofar as in formal abstraction the specific element, whether it be substantial or accidental, is grasped as the positive content of cognition, the result is, materially speaking, the same as that of total abstraction; hence I may refer here to no. 2 of the preceding section, in which it was shown that total abstraction does not imply a falsification of reality. Of course, one should not think that in reality such an abstract cognitive content exists as such i.e. as it is present in the intellect.

Likewise, there will be no falsification of reality when formal abstraction supplies only a particular part or aspect of a real object as the content of cognition. True, in such a case the real object in question is considered only partially or in a limited respect, but nevertheless there can be an adequate representation of this part or aspect of the object. Of course, care should be taken to consider neither such partial views as intentional representations of the whole reality nor the whole reality merely as the sum total of the known aspects or parts.

Because such a partial formal abstraction gives rise to a concept that is an intentional seizure of a definite aspect, while others are not considered and left behind, it will be possible to define such a concept without making reference to the total essence or the non-considered aspects of the object. For instance, the concept 'color' does not mention the object, say, the rose, apple, or paint, from which it has originated, and likewise says nothing about the other aspects or qualities of the objects, such as its shape, dimension or hardness. In a similar way the definitions of mathematical concepts which are drawn from experience by means of formal abstraction are free from any elements that could remind us of these data of experience.

4. *Formal Abstraction, Universality, and Necessity*

Insofar as formal abstraction refers to the specific form, the result is, materially speaking, the same as that of the total abstraction considered in the preceding section. In such a case it gives rise to concepts that are really universal, and leads to universal judgments or statements which at the same time possess a character of necessity because they express an ontological relation which the formal abstraction has discovered to exist in things.

As we will see in the chapter concerning scientific induction (Ch. VIII), in the experiential sciences it is often very difficult to discover the essential and to separate the ontologically necessary from the contingent. In these sciences formal abstraction is often reached only in a laborious way, through an extensive investigation by means of certain scientific methods.

On the other hand, there is also the remarkable phenomenon that the intellect is sometimes able to have a perfect intuitive insight into an aspect of reality which is grasped by formal abstraction and to separate immediately the essential from the non-essential in an intellectual consideration of a single sense datum or phantasm. As was mentioned in No. 1, in such a case the term 'intuitive abstraction' is sometimes used. The immediate result of such an abstraction is a universal judgment expressing a connection that is necessary and is recognized as such. In this way many general insights arise, at least implicitly, in the realm of philosophy and those of the mathematical or formal sciences; for instance, general metaphysical principles, such as those of contradiction and causality; mathematical principles, such as 'the extended is divisible', 'the whole is greater than a part', 'quantities of the same kind may be added to one another', etc. In general one may say that the necessity proper to the mathematical sciences is wholly based upon formal abstraction. Because a good understanding of the various modes of necessity is very important, the next chapter will be devoted to this question.

5. *Formal Abstraction and the Division of the Sciences*

In subsequent pages there will be ample opportunity to point out the importance of formal abstraction in the philosophy of science. Here we want to make only a few remarks regarding the role which by its very nature formal abstraction must play in the division of the sciences. First of all, the formal consideration of always different aspects of the same object may give rise to new areas of study having their own method, so that new sciences can arise, each with its own 'formal object'. The specification of sciences according to their formal objects will be discussed in Chapter Five.

Secondly, a difference in the nature of the formal abstraction used in a science can even be the source of different scientific levels, and thus give rise to a division of the sciences according to levels of abstraction. This question will be considered in section four of this chapter.

6. *Formal and Total Abstraction*

It seems advisable to indicate more fully the points of agreement and disagreement between formal and total abstraction, without, however, entering into a discussion of the differences pointed out by Cajetan and others. We will restrict ourselves to a few aspects that are important for the purpose of this study.

In the first place, it is manifest that if the term 'formal abstraction' is applied to sense cognition, this means simply that the senses according to their own nature will select from the offered data of experience that which constitutes for them a suitable cognitive object, while leaving aside the other sensitive aspects. This abstractive operation of itself produces only a concrete sensitive content of knowledge, but not an abstract concept; hence it would be meaningless to speak here of total abstraction.

Likewise, there will be no danger of confusing total and formal abstraction when the term 'formal abstraction' is used to indicate the activity of one who intellectually makes an analytic investigation of the various aspects presented by a concrete datum of experience, such as this individual person according to his physical and mental structure, character, intelligence, etc. The same is true when a group of individual objects is statistically tabulated according to different aspects.

It is only when there is question of the intellectual activity which grasps in a concrete datum the specific or essential elements—elements having the character of universality—that there is reason to reflect upon the agreement and difference between formal and total abstraction. In such cases it is possible that both activities will agree with respect to the result they produce, for in both cases the result is a cognitive content which is stripped of its material and concrete individual aspects and therefore expressable in a universal concept. Nevertheless, even in this case there is a formal difference between the two activities insofar as they express the universal in different respects. The basis of the difference between formal and total abstraction lies precisely in the twofold aspect of the universal, namely, its ontological and logical aspect.[1] Formal abstraction seizes the datum of experi-

---

[1]This chapter had been written before I happened to read the article "In Defense of Total and Formal Abstraction" by Edward D. Simmons, *The New Scholasticism*, vol. 29 (1955), pp. 427-440. In this article the author defends the Thomistic origin of the concepts 'total' and 'formal abstraction', although the terms themselves were first used in this sense by Cajetan and John of St. Thomas. In a very clear way the author distinguishes the two forms of abstraction. It is with pleasure that I have taken over a few ideas from his important article.

ence in its intelligible content, and in order to reach this content it divests the material datum of its unintelligible wrappings and therefore also of the concrete and individual form in which it appears. The result is an intelligible content which represents the real datum with respect to its specific character and therefore, in point of fact, is universal in the ontological sense.

Total abstraction, on the other hand, strips the sense datum of its concrete individual appearance—which really amounts to dematerializing it—and seizes that which individual things have in common, namely, the specific essence. The result is a universal concept in the logical sense, i.e. a concept which in its recognized universality contains the individuals representing it and thus constitutes a 'logical whole', so that the content of the concept is applicable to the individuals as its logical inferiors. Both abstractions give rise to a universal concept, but in different respects. "Formal abstraction yields the universal *qua* intelligible, and total abstraction yields the universal *qua* universal (i.e., *qua* communicable)."[2] The reason why with respect to data of experience both abstractions, materially speaking, can lead to the same result is "that individuals of a species of physical beings are individuated by matter so that at least on this level particularity and materiality are coextensive".[3]

IV. DEGREES OF ABSTRACTION

Already in the Middle Ages the division of the sciences according to degrees of abstraction was the object of extensive scientific speculation; for instance in St. Thomas' treatise *in Boethium de Trinitate*[1] and his commentators Cajetan and John of St. Thomas. Although the importance of these speculations is often minimized by modern authors, they have not lost anything of their essential value for the division of the sciences, as will become clear in the following pages. We will limit ourselves again to what is necessary or useful for our purpose.

There are several ways in which it is possible to abstract a formal cognitive content from the sense datum, so that formal abstraction

---

[2]*Loc. cit.*, p. 434.

[3]*Loc. cit.*, p. 438.

[1]The relevant part of this work has been translated into English by Armand Maurer under the title *The Division and Methods of the Sciences,* Toronto, 1953. The interested reader may be referred also to Andrew G. van Melsen, *The Philosophy of Nature,* 2nd ed., Pittsburgh-Louvain, 1954, pp. 90-103.

can even terminate on clearly distinct levels. For this reason, in imitation of their medieval predecessors, philosophers speak of different degrees or levels of abstraction.

1. *First Level of Abstraction or Physical Abstraction*

The real world around us consists of individual and concrete things. In forming intellectual notions of these things as perceived by the senses, man makes abstraction from concrete and individual matter, i.e. he leaves out of consideration all that is concrete and individual (negative aspect) and formally draws forth from the sense data a specific or generic essence (positive aspect). Thus we neglect the differences which mark and distinguish this man from that man, and we positively extract the common essence, which enters into the definition of man, monkey, oxygen, electricity, or whatever else we are considering. The abstraction in question is at the same time total and formal, as appears from the considerations of Section III, no. 6.

It should be noted that the object of scientific knowledge on this level of abstraction depends on matter not only for its existence, but even for its understanding.[2] A man, tree, water, etc. cannot exist without matter, and matter enters into their very definition, at least implicitly.

This mode of abstraction is used in experiential sciences, especially in the physical sciences. Physics, for instance, considers heat, electricity, magnetism, etc. without being particularly interested in this individual electric body, magnet, etc. *qua* individual. Because of its use in the study of nature (Latin: *physica*), this first level of abstraction is also called *physical abstraction*.

In order to prevent misunderstandings, it may be useful to add that all simple experiential concepts are obtained by means of direct abstraction from the data of experience; e.g., concepts such as extended whole, part, man, iron, round, white, hard. Usually, the clarity of concepts obtained in this way is limited; it may suffice to distinguish such concepts from one another, but does not suffice to give a clear picture of the objective contents of the concept. Most scientific concepts are not obtained by direct abstraction from experience. Usually they are complex concepts, resulting from various preceding judgments which were obtained through scientific induction or deduction. For example, the concept of iron which the scientist

---

[2]*In Boethium de Trinitate,* V, 1; English translation, pp. 7 f.

has is very different from that of a non-scientist. For a scientist, iron is a metal having a certain color, hardness, elasticity, conductivity of heat, definite magnetic properties, a specific weight of 7.9, an atomic weight of 56, definite chemical properties, etc. All these characteristics enter into his concept of iron and are the result of scientific induction. However, it remains true that the elements themselves which enter into such a complex scientific concept have been obtained through physical abstraction.

2. *Second Level of Abstraction or Mathematical Abstraction*

Abstraction, taken in its negative aspect, may go further than just described and leave out of consideration all sensible conditions of a thing, all sensible matter, i.e. matter "insofar as it is subject to sense qualities, such as being hot or cold, hard or soft, and things of the sort".[3] In this way there remains, to be formally abstracted, quantity, in the double sense of continuous and discrete quantity, or extension and multitude or number. Although extension and multitude or number are abstracted from matter, they remain something imaginable, something which our imagination can readily grasp. Quantity "can be considered in substance before the sensible qualities, in virtue of which matter is called sensible, are understood in it. Quantity, then, does not depend on sensible matter with regard to the nature of its substance, but only on intelligible matter",[4] i.e. on "substance insofar as it is subject to quantity".[5] Thus the objects of scientific knowledge on this level "although depending on matter with respect to their existence, do not depend on it with respect to their concept".[6]

This mode of abstraction is called the second degree or second level of abstraction. It gives rise to the mathematical, formal or ideal sciences. For this reason it is called also *mathematical abstraction*. In the second volume of this work the difference between physical and mathematical abstraction will be seen to be important if we want to obtain a clear understanding of the difference between mathematical and physical sciences.

---

[3]St. Thomas, *Summa theol.,* p. I, q. 85, a. 1, *ad* 2.
[4]*In Boethium de Trinitate,* V, 3; transl. p. 29.
[5]*Summa theol.,* p. I, q. 85, a. 1, *ad* 2.
[6]*In Boethium de Trinitate,* V, 1; transl. p. 8.

3. *Third Level of Abstraction or Metaphysical Abstraction*

Our negative abstraction, finally, can leave out of consideration not merely individual matter (as in physical abstraction) and sensible matter (as in mathematical abstraction), but even so-called 'intelligible matter'. Thus abstraction is made from all matter, so that what remains to be considered by the intellect is purely immaterial.[7]

The object to be considered by scientific knowledge on this level is things "whether they never exist in matter, e.g., God and the angels, or whether they exist in matter in some things and in others do not, e.g., substance, quality, being, potency, act, one and many, and the like",[8] or in general "separate substances and what is common to all beings".[9]

This mode of abstraction is called the third level or degree of abstraction. It gives rise to metaphysical science. For this reason it is called also *metaphysical abstraction*.[10]

Thus we see that the data of sense experience permit various degrees of formal intellectual abstraction according to the precise object which the intellect wants to consider formally in the observed things. Hence it may be said that the differences according to degrees of abstraction are at the same time differences in formal object, at least if the formal object is taken in a rather generic sense.

4. *Levels of Abstraction and Cognitive Functions*

With the difference in level of abstraction there is connected a difference in the role played by man's cognitive faculties of the senses, the imagination, and the intellect. While it is true that "the beginning of all our knowledge is in the sense",[11] the level on which this knowledge terminates may be different. "Sometimes it terminates in the sense, sometimes in the imagination, and sometimes in the

---

[7]To prevent confusion, we wish to remark that also on the other two levels of abstraction the concepts are immaterial, but, contrary to what may happen on the third level, they represent something material.

[8]*Ibid.;* transl., p. 8. Things which never exist in matter are *positively immaterial,* whereas things which exist in matter but are not considered insofar as they are material may be called *immaterial by precision.*

[9]*Op. cit.,* VI, 1, q. 3; transl., p. 59.

[10]To prevent misunderstanding, it is necessary to remark that the concept of being with which metaphysics is concerned results from a very special kind of abstraction, an *abstractio sui generis, per modum expliciti et impliciti,* by way of the explicit and the implicit. It is an imperfect formal abstraction, because everything without exception, even that from which 'abstraction' is made, falls under the concept of being.

[11]*In Boethium de Trinitate,* VI, 2; transl., p. 63.

intellect alone".[12] This concise statement of St. Thomas may be developed as follows. All human knowledge starts with data gathered by sense experience, which by way of the imagination are offered to the consideration of the intellect, which in its activity is dependent upon the imagination. Thus any human intellectual knowledge is brought about through the collaboration of the senses, imagination, and intellect, but the nature of the role played by each of them differs essentially according to the level of abstraction. Regarding this role, we may say the following:

1. On the first level of scientific knowledge, which "terminates in the sense", we "judge of natural things as the sense reveals them. . . . And the person who neglects the senses in regard to natural things falls into error".[13] Hence physical sciences, which consider the data of sense experience, must always be open to verification by sense experience. The same is true for cultural sciences, although in a somewhat different sense. Accordingly, in experiential sciences the contribution made by sense experience is absolutely essential because the object considered is on the sense level. But all three, senses, imagination, and intellect collaborate in the formation of experiential science.

2. On the second level of scientific knowledge, which "terminates in the imagination", sense experience is still needed, but only to provide the imagination with the working material necessary for the formation of phantasms. The essential contribution is made by the imagination because the object is considered on the level of the imagination. In the formation of mathematical science and other branches of learning which are on this level of scientific knowledge it is especially the imagination and the intellect which collaborate.

3. On the third level of scientific knowledge, which "terminates in the intellect", the activity of the senses and the imagination is still needed, but only to make the activity of the intellect possible. The essential contribution can be made only by the intellect because the object considered can be reached only by the intellect. Hence in the formation of metaphysical science only the intellect plays the essential role.

------

[12] *Ibid.*
[13] *Ibid.*

Schema of the Levels of Abstraction

level of abstraction	negative aspect of abstraction	positive aspect of abstraction	genus of speculative sciences	cognitive faculties which have a hold on the object
first level	Abstracts from the individual and the concrete (i.e. from individual matter)	Abstracts the specific essences of sense-perceptible objects (specific qualities and characteristics); the specific essence of material beings or sensible matter	experiential or factual sciences, especially physical sciences	senses imagination intellect
second level	Abstracts from all sensible qualities, but not from quantity (i.e. from sensible matter)	Abstracts quantity insofar as it is countable and measurable (multitude and extension), intelligible matter; in a wider sense, ideal or formal essences	mathematical sciences / in a wider sense, formal or ideal sciences	imagination intellect
third level	Abstracts from all matter (individual, sensible, intelligible)	Abstracts the immaterial (whether positively immaterial or immaterial by precision); being in general	metaphysics	intellect

5. *Abstraction and Knowability*

The distinction of several degrees of formal abstraction is coupled with a distinction in degrees of knowability. Because the proper object of the human intellect is the immaterial in sense-perceptible material reality, the intelligibility of an object will correspond with its degree of immateriality and therefore with its degree of abstraction from matter. Accordingly, a threefold degree of intelligibility corresponds with the three degrees of abstraction from matter and immateriality. Hence with respect to the object of man's intellectual knowledge we may distinguish three genera of objects:

1. *Sense-perceptible* beings (the world around us), which are knowable by the senses, the imagination, and the intellect. They belong to the first level of abstraction and are the subject matter of the experiential sciences.

2. *Ideal* or *imaginable* beings, especially quantity (extension and multitude), which are knowable by the imagination and the intellect. They belong to the second level of abstraction and constitute the object of mathematics and in general of ideal or formal sciences. This group of sciences has an advantage over the preceding group insofar as its object does not have the lack of transparency of material things, and over the following group insofar as the intellect finds the required support in more adequate phantasms.

3. Being in general or *immaterial* being (whether positively immaterial or rendered immaterial by precision from matter), which is knowable only by the intellect because it is not imaginable. It belongs to the third level of abstraction and is the object of metaphysics. Concerning this object it is to be noted that, although the immaterial is more knowable in itself, it is less knowable to man, because it cannot be properly represented by phantasms from which man's intellect takes its proper object.[14]

Remark. It is to be noted that progressive *total* abstraction yields concepts whose content decreases steadily and thus becomes more general, vaguer and consequently less knowable.

6. *Gradation on the Same Level of Abstraction*

Even on the same level of abstraction a certain gradational difference is possible, as may be clear from the following examples. On the third level of abstraction there is a gradational difference between pure metaphysics and the philosophy of nature. On the second level there is gradation inasmuch as in arithmetic or the theory of multitude abstraction goes further than in geometry or the theory of extension, for the notion of multitude is not limited to extended things. Therefore, the notion of multitude is predicable of spirits, but not so the notion of extension. On the first level of abstraction there is gradation in physical sciences; for example, inasmuch as the object of

---

[14]Cf. *In Boethium de Trinitate,* VI, 1 and 2; transl., pp. 46 ff.

biology is less abstract than that of physics or general astronomy. In cultural sciences there is generally less abstraction than in the physical sciences. However, even among cultural sciences themselves some are more abstract than others; e.g. sociology and economics are more abstract than history.

Even within one and the same science a gradation of abstraction and generality is possible. For example, in astronomy one can consider celestial bodies in general and their classes, but also individual celestial bodies, such as the sun, the moon, or the Crab nebula.

V. SIMPLIFYING OR IDEALIZING ABSTRACTION

Description. As the name itself indicates, this kind of abstraction is one by which abstraction is made from the complicating elements in a complex whole (negative aspect) in order to consider the resulting simplified object (positive aspect of abstraction). Such a simplifying abstraction is often used in the experiential sciences in order to make it possible to study a problem of reality which is too complex to be studied if all the factors involved have to be taken into account. Let us give a few examples. In the kinetic theory of gases the molecules are treated as if they were perfect little spheres endowed with perfect elasticity, and in addition their dimensions and mutual attraction are often left out of consideration. A gas composed of such molecules is called an 'ideal gas' by the physicist. In mechanics the friction of the air is often neglected in the consideration of free falling bodies or the path of a bullet. In chemistry they speak of 'pure substances', although it is known that such substances do not exist in reality. In many astronomical speculations celestial bodies are treated as if they were point-masses. In cultural sciences, likewise, many such simplifying abstractions are made; e.g. if in studying groups of people one leaves out of consideration their individual differences of age, origin, financial status, religion, etc.

This Abstraction Falsifies Reality. Contrary to what happens in formal and total abstraction, idealizing abstraction is always a falsification of reality, for the objects considered are different from those in reality. For instance, the real molecules of gases do not have a perfect spherical shape; they have definite and often irregular dimensions and attract one another. Hence in order to be certain that the results obtained by means of idealizing abstraction retain any value for the description or explanation of reality, it will be necessary to examine very carefully whether the simplifications in question are permissible with respect to the problem under consideration. Frequently only confrontation with the data of experience will show whether or not the simplifications are justified.

Remark. It is to be noted that simplifying abstraction presupposes at least the first degree of formal abstraction. If the problem in question is studied quantitatively, it presupposes also the second degree. The objects considered are simplified or idealized in such a way that certain concepts obtained by formal abstraction of the first or second degree are applicable to these objects. Of course, the concepts used in simplifying abstraction are abstract also in the sense that they do not include individual and concrete particularities. Thus formal and total abstraction remain the most fundamental of all types of abstraction.

CHAPTER FOUR

NECESSITY IN SCIENCE

In nos. 3 and 5 of Chapter Two it was explained that the principles of a science are always expressed in universal propositions; that the results of scientific research are preferably formulated in the same way; and that this universal character corresponds with the necessity of the connection between the concepts expressing the subject and the predicate of the proposition. In the preceding chapter we have seen that the universality and character of necessity flow from the total or formal abstraction by means of which the knowing intellect eliminates the singularizing determinations of the concrete object and draws forth from it the essential or some other knowable 'form'. This character of necessity will be discussed in several other parts of this book, and especially in the second volume when the various kinds of sciences are studied. However, even at this stage it appears desirable to present a general consideration of necessity, because it is a characteristic feature of science, which, just as universality, belongs to the statements of every science, although in different ways. Again, however, our discussion will be limited to what is relevant for the purpose of this book.

Necessary in the strict sense is called everything that cannot not-be or be different. According as this definition is verified without restrictions or only under certain conditions or in a definite order, a distinction is made between *absolute* and *hypothetical* necessity. We will successively consider both types here.

I. ABSOLUTE NECESSITY

Absolute or metaphysical necessity is present in a proposition if, under no condition, the connection between subject and predicate can be other than is expressed in the proposition. It is this necessity that is encountered in general metaphysical principles, such as the principles of identity, of contradiction, of sufficient reason, of causality (as applied to the four causes); also the principle of determinism, which is valid for every purely material activity and according to which every non-free cause produces of necessity its own effect. As special formulations of some of these principles one may consider the

35

principles 'every being has its own essential properties' and 'action follows being'. The last two principles, which refer especially to formal and material causes, are also absolutely valid and can be applied in many realms. By way of illustration we may give a few examples: an extended thing is necessarily divisible; the whole is greater than the part; the sum of two quantities of the same kind is another quantity of the same kind; a hylomorphically composite whole is by its very nature subject to change; a spiritual being is necessarily endowed with the powers of thinking and willing, etc. All these necessities are absolute because, apart from the presence of the essence indicated by the subject of the proposition, they do not depend upon any condition in the things themselves or their surroundings. Many of such universal principles have been discovered in a concrete sense datum through formal or intuitive abstraction. Nevertheless our intellect sees that the truth of such statements does not depend upon the actual existence of the essence in question. If an extended thing exists, it will be divisible precisely because of its extension; if a spirit exists, he will be able to think and will.

II. HYPOTHETICAL NECESSITY

Apart from the above-mentioned statements that are valid with absolute necessity, there are others which possess likewise a certain character of necessity, but are so much dependent upon a definite order or definite presuppositions that they are almost meaningless outside the order in question. Such statements can be formulated only after a more accurate exploration and study of the order in question or only upon the basis of the assumed presuppositions, which therefore are always implied in them. They are said to be *hypothetically necessary*. This hypothetical character is not always understood in the same sense, and care should be taken not to misconceive it. A subdivision into three groups is possible here according to the realms of thought in which the statements originate. These realms are that of mathematics or formal sciences (the mathematical order), that of the physical sciences (the physical order), and that of man and his culture (the moral order). Let us briefly consider each one of these three necessities.

1. *Necessity in the Mathematical Order or Mathematical Necessity*

According to an absolutely valid principle stated in Section One, the inner structure or proper essence of mathematical objects implies of necessity certain essential characteristics or relations; for instance, a triangle necessarily has three angles; the sum of two numbers is of necessity another number. These and other similar truths are often discovered in the data of experience by means of formal and intuitive abstraction. If it is desirable to speak here in terms of causality, the inner necessity of the relations discovered in mathematics may be reduced to formal causality. For it is the 'form', shape, structure, or mathematical entity which 'produces' of necessity definite essential characteristics and relations. But to a high degree mathematical entities are products of the human mind, and this shows their hypothetical character.

In mathematics, as also in other formal sciences, such as logistics, the strictly hypothetical character often reveals itself very clearly—namely, when the essence of the object, and therefore also the implied inner necessity, is co-determined by arbitrarily chosen conventions or postulates. A few examples will suffice to make this clear. It is only in Euclidean geometry, because of the postulate of parallel lines, that the sum of the three angles of a triangle is equal to two right angles; in a non-Euclidean triangle the sum is greater or smaller than that of two right angles. With respect to other geometrical objects different statements result according as one assumes the postulates of Euclid or those of Riemann or Lobatschewski. The sum of 3 and 4 is 7 if natural numbers are meant, but e.g. in the case of vectors of the magnitudes of 3 and 4, the sum will depend upon their directions. The sum will be 7 if the vectors run in the same direction; 1 if they run in opposite directions; 5 if their directions are perpendicular; different again if they have another position with respect to one another. Hence in this case the mutual position or geometric situation is a condition that must be mentioned in order that the correct answer may be given, but under this condition the answer will apply with necessity.

2. *Necessity in the Physical Order or Physical Necessity*

The term 'physical necessity' indicates the necessity that is proper to statements which are the result of a scientifically digested experience regarding the things of nature. The term 'things of nature' refers to all lifeless and living objects, except man insofar as his activities can be freely determined by his will. Accordingly, we are concerned here with objects whose activities are fully determined, i.e. their activities are fully fixed with respect to time, character, and intensity by the proper nature of the things in question as they are concretely situated. Hence in this order we have to do with a causality that works according to a necessity of nature. A corresponding necessity, therefore, is proper to statements regarding the properties and activities of the things of nature, provided, of course, that these statements have been arrived at in a correct way. This type of necessity finds its foundation in the material and formal causes whose combination (as 'formed matter') constitutes the essence of the things in question.

Such statements occur in the laws of physics, chemistry, biology, etc. These laws, if they are correctly defined, express a connection which is necessarily true and cannot be other. However—and here lies the 'hypothetical' character—this necessity is an *observed* necessity, i.e. it is not based upon a direct intellectual insight into the essence of things, but upon an experience which has been subjected to scientific methods. In addition, the statements refer to the order of the world as it is at this moment actually accessible to the experience of man with the means he has now at his disposal. They are true if we suppose that our experience has not been deceptive, and that the results obtained have been formulated correctly; therefore, they will remain true if we suppose that this order of the world is not subject to change in its essential constituent elements. But there is a possibility of another world order with different kinds of material things and therefore with different laws. Accordingly, one can speak neither of absolute necessity in the above-explained sense nor of the necessity that is found in the mathematical order. The special character of the necessity under consideration is suitably expressed by the term 'physical necessity'.

In the domain of the physical sciences the intellect works again with formal abstraction, but because of the complexity of the object and the difficulty of approaching it there can be no question here of abstractive intuition. Frequently the 'formal' element has to be discovered here in a gradual and laborious way, sometimes only after many vain attempts and even errors.[1] Thus in this respect there is a great difference between the physical and mathematical sciences.

------

[1]The methods used in this process of discovery will be discussed in our study of scientific induction (Chapter Eight).

3. *Necessity in the Order of Human Activities or Moral Necessity*

Moral Necessity in the Strict Sense. Although man is free in the activities of his rational will, such activity is not purely arbitrary but based upon motives and directed towards the attainment of a purpose. It may happen that man must or wants to reach a definite purpose. In this case his way of acting is determined by the purpose intended. Thus we arrive at a necessary connection which may be expressed in a conditional sentence: 'If man must or wants to reach this definite purpose, he will of necessity have to direct his actions in this determined way'.

The purpose or end to which all activity of man in general must be directed is his ultimate end. To reach this end, he will have to live and work in accordance with the demands of man's rational nature. The necessary connection in question can be expressed in the conditional sentence: 'If man wants to reach his ultimate end, he will have to act in accordance with the demands of his rational nature'. Starting from a comprehensive consideration of man's ultimate end, insofar as this is possible with the aid of natural reason and the data of Revelation, moral philosophers and theologians know how to derive specific norms of human activity which must necessarily be followed if the ultimate end is to be reached. Because we are here in the realm of the moral order in the strict sense of the term, the expression 'moral necessity' obviously is a suitable term.

Moral Necessity in a Broader Sense. The same term is used also in a broader sense and applied to human actions in general, including those that tend to limited purposes which are only remotely connected with the ultimate end or even indifferent in its respect. The purposes in question lie in the natural plane and can be the occasion for definite human activities. Here again it is possible to formulate specific norms—it is done in the so-called 'practical sciences'—which of necessity have to be followed in the matter in question, at least if the purpose intended is to be reached.

Moral Necessity in the Broadest Sense. Finally, the term is used in a third way to express the necessity proper to statements regarding the way in which as a matter of fact man acts in a definite sphere or in definite circumstances. Such statements may be the result of scientific research in those sciences of experience whose object is man and his culture. Because in general man tends to his own happiness, whether supernatural or natural, it will be possible to find in similar circumstances of religion, culture, social and financial status, profession, age, etc. a certain uniformity of action which can be expressed in definite rules or laws possessing a kind of necessity. Because there is question here of moral activity in the broad sense, i.e. of human manners and morals, the term 'moral necessity' is used here. As examples we may give the following rules: parents love their children; in a religiously mixed population men live more consciously in accordance with their beliefs; unrestricted capitalism tends to the exploitation of the workers; if demand increases considerably, prices will rise; etc.

Nature of this Moral Necessity. Obviously, the above-mentioned moral necessity, proper to rules governing certain types of human activities which individually find their ultimate source in a free choice, is wholly different from the physical necessity that arises from the determined nature of material things. While physical necessity knows no exception, this moral necessity allows many. These exceptions may originate in the defective intellectual insight of the individual concerned into the purpose to be reached or the means to be used, in a lack of training of the will, or the influence of all kind of emotional factors. Consequently, such *rules* of human activity do not give any certainty with respect to the actions of a particular individual at a definite time, but they justify an expectation which, if large numbers are considered, will be fulfilled in most cases. The degree of necessity proper to such rules will be proportioned to the importance men attach to the purpose which determines their activity. For instance, in the natural order the preservation of life is more important as a purpose than the preservation or acquisition of material possessions; consequently, in practice the rules governing human activity with respect to the preservation of one's own life will have fewer exceptions than the rules regarding the preservation or acquisition of material possessions.

Moral Necessity and the Conclusions of Moral Sciences. The fact that general rules can be given which possess a certain necessity with respect to the rational activities of man's will gives rise to the possibility of sciences that have as their object man's activities in different realms. Such sciences may be either practical, as the ethical and medical sciences, or theoretical, as psychology, ethnology, sociology or theoretical economics. On the other hand, the possibility of exceptions on the rules and that of mistakes with respect to the subjective purposive orientations of individual human beings and their efforts to reach these purposes imply the danger of error in drawing conclusions in these sciences. The so-called proofs and scientific conclusions of such sciences have another degree of certainty and validity than those proper to the mathematical or physical sciences. Moreover, there is great danger of falling into subjectivity. In the second volume we will return to this point in our discussion of the sciences of man and his culture.

III. NECESSITY AND CONTINGENCY

'Contingency' Has Several Meanings. It appears desirable to add here at the end of this chapter a few remarks regarding contingency. According to the scientific usage of the terms, 'contingency' and 'necessity' indicate contradictory concepts, so that 'contingent' means the same as 'non-necessary'. Thus it should be clear that 'contingent' may have different meanings, because there are also different kinds of necessities. Moreover, the meaning of the term 'contingent' is never absolute but always relative. Thus a fully justified use of the term will always require an addition explaining in what sense there is contingency.

Contingency and Necessity. In general, 'contingent' means that which can be or not-be, be this or be other. In this broad sense all created things are contingent. Once created, however, they have a specific essence which necessarily has definite specific properties. Accordingly, with respect to these properties there is no contingency. But the individual and concrete way in which the specific essence appears is not wholly determined by this essence, for one and the same specific essence allows variations with respect to its actual realizations. In this respect therefore there is, within certain limits, contingency. Nevertheless, there is a misunderstanding here that should be avoided. The concrete and individual way in which the essence actually appears is necessary in this case insofar as it is wholly determined by the causes which have determined or are determining the coming to be, the existence, and the mode of being of this thing. Thus with respect to the whole of causes that have been or are at work there is no contingency. Accordingly, a particular event may be contingent with respect to a definite and separately considered cause, but in relation to the complex of causes that exercised influence on this event the event is necessary. For this necessity is the result of the universally valid law of causality.

In this connection special mention must be made of the contingency existing with respect to a free cause, i.e. a cause which is not fully determined by its own nature, such as man's free will. Before the definite decision of the will there is freedom and therefore contingency with respect to its possible actions, but after the actual self-determination the activity will of necessity take a definite course, and thus the contingency is actually eliminated.

CHAPTER FIVE

THE OBJECT OF SCIENCE

1. *Material and Formal Object*

In Chapter Three, Sections Three and Four, we spoke of the intellectual activity, called 'formal abstraction', through which the intellect in various ways is capable of seeing in a datum offered by the senses a knowable essential form or aspect. Thus the offered material is 'formed' or 'informed' in a definite way by the intellect.

The terms 'matter' and 'form', 'material' and 'formal' are used very frequently in philosophy. 'Matter', in general, indicates the undetermined but determinable part of a thing, while 'form' is that by which the matter of a thing is determined to be a thing of a certain kind. For example, marble or plaster may be called 'matter' with respect to the geometric forms by which they are given a definite external shape. Another example is 'primary matter', which is conceived as the most undetermined substratum of all material things, and 'substantial form', which gives to primary matter its first and specific form. Thus 'matter' always indicates the indeterminate but determinable element, and 'form' the determining element. These relative meanings of 'material' and 'formal' are found also in the theory of science where there is question of the 'material object' and the 'formal object' of a science.

Material Object. Each science occupies itself with a definite realm of knowledge, a definite subject matter to be investigated, which is called the 'material object' of that science. As such may be considered, for instance, man, inanimate matter, the stars, the earth, languages, religion, law, etc. Once more we may remark that obviously what is meant here are not men, earth, stars, etc. as they exist in reality, but insofar as they have become a suitable object matter of knowledge by means of the intellectual process of abstraction (total abstraction; cf. Ch. III, Sect. 2).

Formal Object. As a rule, a definite material object that is taken as the general matter to be studied will have too many knowable aspects to be grasped fully in a single intellectual consideration. To arrive at a well-founded total view the man of science will have to try to seize successively in quasi-partial studies, i.e. through formal and analytic abstractions, the various aspects of the object. Accordingly, the object matter, the material object, will have to be determined or 'formed' in various ways. The material object thus 'formed', i.e. the material object considered in a definite respect, is called the 'formal object' of the intellectual consideration.

Because of the complexity of existing realities and their consequent manifoldness with respect to knowable aspects, generally one and the same material object can be multiplied into numerous formal objects. Each of these can be systematically examined and thus give rise to ever new sciences. For instance, the material object 'man' is in different ways the formal object of anatomy, physiology, psychology, physical anthropology, ethnology, medical sciences, philosophical anthropology, and so on. While the material object itself roughly describes the nature and limits of a science, the proper character and structural coherence of a science is derived from its formal object, for this object demands a definite mode of consideration and definite methods of investigation. With respect to the same material object, therefore, every important difference in formal object may give rise to a distinction of sciences. Presently we will revert in more detail to this point.

Formal Object 'Quod' and 'Quo'. A particular object which is investigated requires, precisely because of its particular nature, a particular and appropriate mode of consideration and consequently the use of proper and appropriate means and methods. The formal object which is investigated is usually called the *'formal object quod'*, and the appropriate mode of considering this object is called the *'formal object quo'*. The following scheme may serve to illustrate the point. In this scheme the material object, the formal object *quod*, and the formal object *quo* of a few cognate sciences are placed side by side.

science	material object	formal object *quod*	formal object *quo* (means and methods)
dogmatic theology	God	God as manifested in Revelation	light of Revelation, grace, meditation
philosophy of God	God	God as knowable to man's intellect without Revelation	man's intellect and reasoning
nuclear physics	atomic nuclei	atomic nuclei as knowable by physical methods	physical **mode of** consideration and physical methods
nuclear chemistry	atomic nuclei	atomic nuclei as knowable by chemical methods	chemical mode of consideration and chemical methods

The same distinction may be applied also to parts of a science. For example,

mineralogy	minerals and crystals	crystalline structure	methods of refraction and reflexion, X-rays, etc.
		color	optical methods

2. *Division of Sciences According to the Object*

In Ch. III, Sect. IV, we have seen how the formal abstraction of the intellect may terminate on different levels and thus be the basis of the distinction between major groups or genera of sciences—namely, the experiential sciences; the mathematical, or more generally the formal, sciences; and the philosophical sciences. On each of these levels a division can be made according to the material object, and with respect to the same material object it usually is possible to seize, through formal abstraction, successively different formal objects and to distinguish these objects from one another. This possibility finds expression in a specification of science on the same level and with respect to the same object. We will now consider this question.

Division According to Material Object. As we have seen, the material object gives a certain coherence to a science and thus divides it from other sciences with a different material object. A science of man, for example, is obviously distinguishable from a science of the stars or a science of language. Because of its wide range the material object may force us to divide it into segments; e.g. the science of languages will have to be resolved into sciences of each language separately; and the anatomy of man may be subdivided into that of the brain, the heart, the lungs, etc. These examples indicate divisions and subdivisions according to the material object.

Division According to Formal Object. As has been mentioned, generally a division or subdivision will have its basis in the discovery of new aspects or formal phases in the same material object. In this way we obtain a division or subdivision according to formal object. For instance, the science of the human body may be divided according to the formal object into anatomy, physiology, physical anthropology, pathology, and so on.

Even when at first sight the division appears to have been made so as to divide too wide an object into smaller segments, or apparently only according to the material object, a closer inspection will reveal that the reason why this and no other division is made lies in the fact that the segments in question represent different aspects of reality or demand a different mode of consideration. Hence in such a case the division will be based also upon a difference in formal object. These observations should be kept in mind in the following examples of division of science.

Examples of Division and Subdivision of Sciences According to Material and/or Formal Objects

A. *Physical Sciences*

   a) *sciences of inanimate matter*
   physics, chemistry, astronomy, geology, meteorology, mineralogy, etc.

   subdivision of physics
   optics, acoustics, thermodynamics, electricity, magnetism, etc.

   subdivision of chemistry
   organic chemistry, inorganic chemistry

   subdivision of astronomy according to material object
   astronomy of stars, nebulae, planets, comets, sun, moon, etc.

according to material and formal object

astrophysics, celestial mechanics, position astronomy (each of which has its own methods and mode of consideration).

b) *sciences of animate matter*

botany, zoology.

It is clear that zoology insofar as it deals also with sense life differs from botany not only according to the material object but also according to the formal object.

B. *Cultural Sciences*

sociology, ethnology, political science, juridical science, linguistics, science of religions, etc.

In the case of cultural sciences, too, the material object alone does not always give rise to a rigorous separation, but the formal object also enters into the picture.

subdivision of linguistics

Roman, Germanic, Celtic, classical, general linguistics, etc.

Subdivision of juridical science

constitutional law, state law, criminal law, maritime law, civil law, etc.

These differences, too, are not merely material but at the same time formal.

C. *Mathematical Sciences*

geometry, trigonometry, arithmetic, algebra, etc.

The difference between the mathematical sciences is more formal than material.

D. *Physical and Cultural Sciences*

The important division of experiential sciences into physical and cultural sciences and sciences of man is, as we will see in the second volume, a division according to the material object, but extends over the formal object because with respect to these sciences the difference in material object is at the same time a difference in formal object.

E. *Philosophy*

metaphysics, epistemology, anthropology, cosmology, aesthetics, ethics, etc.

The various branches of philosophy are not wholly separate; all things are closely interwoven in philosophy.

Remarks. With respect to these examples of division of sciences according to the object, a few remarks may be added. Most often, as appears from the examples given, a division according to the material object is combined with a consideration of different aspects of the material object; therefore, it is concurrent with a division according to the formal object, as for example, the division of chemistry into organic and inorganic. Sometimes the distinction is more formal than material, as in the case of the mathematical sciences.

Very often sciences are distinct only because they have different ways of considering the same material object. In such a case they are divided according to their formal object only and not according to their material object; e.g. analytic and synthetic geometry; the anatomy and physiology of the human body; epistemology and the psychology of human knowledge.

At times it may happen that division and subdivisions according to the material object run across those according to the formal object; and vice versa, as may be illustrated by the following schema.

Subdivision of History

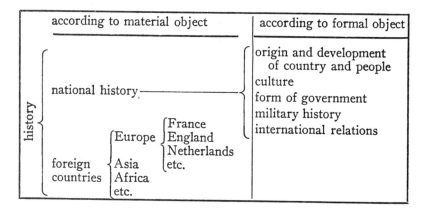

The division according to formal object, given above for national history, may be made also with respect to each foreign country; hence a division of history according to culture, form of government, military history, etc. would run across that according to country or material object.

3. *Specialization and Integration*

As a result of the enormous increase of data and the invention of new methods of investigation and experimentation, the whole of science had to be divided over and over again according to material and formal objects. The material object has become steadily more and more divided into smaller parts, and each of these in its turn can still be considered under various aspects. This cutting up of the realm of science has given rise to a subordination of sciences and an ever-increasing specialization of science and scientists. Because of their divergent methods of procedure and investigation, these specialists often were and are hardly able to understand one another's language. Thus it is easy to see that a need arose for integration and synthesis in the realm of science. Specialists of different sciences came together to study a small object or question from all angles. In this way was brought about a collaboration of scientists working as a team; e.g. physicians working together as a lung team or a heart team consisting of an anatomist, a physiologist, a medical chemist, an anesthetist, etc.

On the other hand, there are specialists who restrict themselves to a very small material object, which, however, they consider and study under all aspects. For example, a brain specialist or a heart specialist has a command of the anatomy, physiology, neurology, and surgery of the brain or the heart; he not only makes the diagnosis, but also performs the necessary surgery, prescribes the diet, and so on.

CHAPTER SIX

THE FOUNDATION OF SCIENCE

1. *Starting Point and Presuppositions*

As we have seen in Chapter Two, a science is always a logically ordered system, i.e. the various parts of a science are logically coherent. One part is based upon another or justified by another part. Scientific statements are deduced by reasoning from other statements, and these perhaps again from others. Evidently, this process cannot be continued to infinity. Ultimately one will arrive at premises that no longer are conclusions of a reasoning process within the limits of a given science, but have their truth established in another way, such as their direct observation by the senses or their foundation in another science. Somehow every science is bound to have fundamental data that can serve as the starting point of scientific demonstrations. As Aristotle correctly observes in the opening sentence of his *Analytica Posteriora,* "All instruction given or received by way of argument proceeds from pre-existent knowledge".[1] Although this starting point of science may be called its basis or foundation, it would seem preferable to use the term 'foundation' in a wider sense and thus to make a distinction between starting point and foundation. We will use the term 'foundation' to indicate everything which in one way or the other, explicitly or implicitly, can be considered as a basic element in the scientific system. Accordingly, the foundation of a science includes not only its starting point but also its presuppositions. A brief consideration will be devoted to each of these two points.

Starting Point. The function of the starting point is to supply the basic data concerning the object considered in the science. Thus the starting point of a science will be of the same nature as the object studied in this science. According as the various sciences differ in character, the starting points also will be typically different. Hence it is not feasible to indicate here exactly the starting points of the various groups of sciences and still less those of any science in particular. We will have to be satisfied therefore with offering a few broad examples to illustrate our point.

---

[1] Bk. I, ch. 1; 71a 1-2, as translated in W. D. Ross, *The Works of Aristotle.*

Examples. The physical sciences take their starting point in the concrete data of the senses that are obtained by means of direct observation or experimentation. The various physical sciences differ again with respect to their particular starting point. Physics and chemistry begin with the sense observation of lifeless things, such as solids, liquids and gases with respect to their general or special qualities and activities; e.g. sound, light, heat, electric and magnetic properties, in general or in different species of matter; and the chemical qualities of the various kinds of matter. Geology and astronomy are based upon the experience of the earth and that of celestial bodies. Biological sciences derive their starting point from experience regarding plants and animals. In addition, insofar as the theoretical study of their object is concerned, the physical sciences have to reconstruct or introduce certain concepts which are suitable for the description of natural phenomena and whose meaning is fixed by a definition or a functional relationship; for instance, in physics the concepts of force, velocity, energy, mass, and magnitudes of a mechanical, electric, or magnetic nature.

The sciences of man have a broader starting point. It is constituted not only by sense experience but also by man's intellectual reflection upon himself, by means of which he obtains a higher kind of knowledge of his own specific and individual nature and thus is rendered capable also of *Einfühling,* i.e. 'putting himself in the place of' the other human beings with whom he is in contact.

The cultural sciences begin with a sense observation and an intellectual consideration of all the things produced by man's typically human activities, which are labeled together under the term 'culture'. Here again there is a pronounced difference with respect to the starting point between the various cultural sciences, such as history, linguistics, science of law, sociology, and economy.

In the mathematical sciences the starting point is provided by definite fundamental concepts, such as multitude (or number) and extension, either in general or in special kinds of extended things, e.g. line, surface, or body; definite fundamental axioms or postulates, which may be chosen somewhat arbitrarily; and finally all kinds of data of the imagination, aided by the sense observation of, e.g., figures drawn on paper, which function as means in the discovery and solution of new problems.

The philosophical sciences have their starting point in an intellectual reflection on the general data of experience with respect to the being of man and things outside man.   The theological sciences find theirs in the data of Revelation.

Presuppositions. Apart from the starting point that is needed in every science, also numerous presuppositions must be admitted. Generally these presuppositions are not formulated explicitly, but admitted implicitly and accepted as a matter of course.   More often than not specialists in a science do not know anything at all about the presuppositions of their particular science or group of cognate sciences, and are not even interested in them.

It would lead us too far afield to investigate here the presuppositions of the various sciences.   A complete enumeration of all these presuppositions would even be impossible.   Hence we will have to be satisfied again with a few general remarks and examples.

General Presuppositions. First of all, a distinction must be made between presuppositions that are common to all or many sciences and those that are proper to a particular science or group of sciences.   To the first class of presuppositions belong those which are expressed in metaphysical principles, for these principles apply to whatever is as such; for instance, the principles of identity, contradiction, and excluded middle; the principles of sufficient reason and causality; also epistemological presuppositions regarding the intelligibility of being, the trustworthiness of the human intellect, and with respect to all sciences that somehow originate in experience, the trustworthiness of the senses and sense memory.   These and other similar principles and presuppositions cannot be deduced from more general or more evident principles, but only made explicit by the intellect which reflects upon primary contents of cognition.

Special Presuppositions. Secondly, the particular sciences or groups of sciences have their own presuppositions regarding their own object.   Such special presuppositions will find a foundation in another specialized science or in philosophy.   Without entering into detail, we may give some examples of particular presuppositions in a few sciences. In physical sciences, *i.a.,* the following presuppositions are accepted: the determinism of nature, the uniformity of matter in space and time, the species-individual structure of matter; and with respect to the mathematical study of quantitative results, the truth of mathematical theorems.   In linguistics one has to accept certain fundamental notions concerning substance, accidents, activities, the difference of individuals, etc., in order to be able to have an insight into the meaning of substantives, adjectives, verbs, personal and other pronouns, etc. In mathematics it is necessary to presuppose everything which precedes the formation of the first mathematical notions, elementary axioms and operations; e.g. that the extended is divisible; that the whole is greater than its parts; that quantities of the same kind may be added, and that the sum total is a quantity of the same kind. In theology one presupposes the truth of Revelation, the veracity of the sources of Revelation, and the veracity of God.

2. *Truth of the Foundation of a Science*

It should be clear that no particular science is able to justify by its own means and methods the truth of its own foundation, i.e. of either its starting point or its presuppositions. Physical science, for example, cannot by its own means account for the existence of observed facts and phenomena, for the truth of mathematical theorems, or the principle of causality or determinism in nature. Mathematics cannot account for the fundamental qualities of extension and quantity. Even in modern mathematics, in which the starting point consists of certain postulates chosen arbitrarily (for they have to be merely independent of one another and non-contradictory), it is not possible to do without presuppositions or data which cannot be accounted for by the mathematical system itself.

Sometimes, as was said above, it is possible for one science to justify the presuppositions of another. For example, the value of writings and documents containing the starting point of theology can be accounted for by the historical methods used in the so-called '*preambula fidei*'; the determinism of nature presupposed by physical science can be shown to be true by philosophy; the existence of free will in man, that is presupposed by the sciences of man and of human culture, can be discussed in philosophical anthropology; the fundamental axioms of Euclidean geometry can be accounted for by reflection upon the fundamental data of the senses and imagination as they are rendered accessible to the intellect by formal abstraction on the second level. The most fundamental metaphysical and epistemological principles, however, which have to be presupposed in all human science cannot at all be proved, at least not syllogistically, i.e. by taking other principles as a starting point. Such principles can be clarified only by making explicit what the intellect discovers in its reflection upon primary data of experience.

3. *Starting Point and Division of Science*

The difference in the starting point of sciences or in the origin of their basic notions and truths gives rise to an important division of science. According as this origin is supernatural or natural, i.e. provided by Revelation or by man's natural cognitive faculties of the senses, imagination, and intellect, science can be divided into supernatural and natural. The starting point of science likewise marks the difference between mathematical and experiential science. However, this is not the place to discuss these divisions; so we will be satisfied with having pointed out that there is a connection between the starting point and the division of the sciences. Later, in the second volume of this book, we will come back to this point in greater detail.

4. *Starting Point and Subordination of Sciences*

The consideration of the starting point of natural sciences may give rise to a subordination of sciences in the only true sense of the term. True subordination occurs if the principles that are the basis of one science are investigated and established in another; therefore, a subordinated science gets its support from the subordinating science and to some extent owes its special character to this science. A case in point is physics, which makes use of principles and theorems established by mechanics and mathematics, and also of presuppositions, such as the principles of causality and determinism, that can be justified only by philosophy. So also the theory of music to some extent is governed by mathematics; medical and agricultural sciences are ruled by physics and chemistry. Nevertheless, subordinated sciences have their own special methods and examine their object in a way that is characteristically their own and different from that of the sciences (e.g. mathematics or philosophy in the case of physical science) by which some of their principles are established. Thus even subordinated sciences have their own autonomy and retain special features which mark them as distinct sciences.

CHAPTER SEVEN

SCIENTIFIC METHODS

INTRODUCTION. METHOD IN GENERAL

The term 'method' is derived from the Greek *'methodos'* ('road to') ; hence etymologically speaking its general meaning is the way or manner of doing or making something, the system of procedure to obtain or reach the end intended. In science 'method' always means the way of procedure from the known to the unknown, from a given starting point to final propositions in a determined field of knowledge. Hence in speculative sciences it indicates the road to propositions concerning that which exists or is thought to exist; whereas in normative sciences it indicates the road to the norms governing the doing or making of something.

It is clear that a good method will always be of the greatest importance. Without such a method, as a rule, no good results will be obtained, at least not without much needless expenditure of effort. According to Descartes' well-known expression, "It is not enough to have a clear mind; the important point is to apply it correctly". i.e. methodically.

Especially in the sciences, the use of correct methods is most important in order to make certain that the conclusions are correctly connected with the starting point and the foundation. For only in this case will the results obtained be able to share in the value and truth of the starting point.

General Rules of Every Scientific Method. Every scientific method is the road from the known starting point to a finishing point or result which in one way or the other is linked to this starting point. This connection can be established in several ways; for example, through logical reasoning or deduction, or through induction, synthesis, or analysis. Before studying these various scientific methods separately, we will first give a few general rules which must be observed in every scientific method.

a) *The starting point must be clear, true, and certain.* Since in science one must always proceed from a starting point, care will have to be taken that this starting point be reliable and clear in all respects.

55

Therefore, steps must be taken to clarify the concepts, render the definitions exact, formulate the postulates unambiguously, etc. In the case of experiential sciences it will be necessary to observe and determine the facts accurately, to separate the pertinent from the impertinent, and to put them into an appropriate order. Briefly, one must see to it that the starting point (antecedents or premises) is clear, true, and certain.

b) *The problems must be made as simple as possible.* In order to make the solution of the problems under investigation possible, generally an effort has to be made to simplify them as much as possible. This simplification can be arrived at by means of a thorough analysis and an appropriate division of the concepts or phenomena concerned, because in this way it will be possible to study separately the various aspects of the object investigated.

c) *Coherence must be maintained.* Because a science must be a coherent system, care must be taken to establish and maintain coherence. From premises, in the wider sense of the term, whose truth and certainty has been established true and certain conclusions must be derived with logical consequence. This coherence is obtained through a careful observance of the general scientific method and through successive and interconnected arguments and proofs.

d) *Well-founded hypotheses are useful.* Although the ideal of science is the attainment of truth and certainty, it will often become necessary to be satisfied with probability regarding one or the other part of the data considered or with probable arguments. Hence the use of hypotheses is permissible and useful, sometimes even necessary. However, hypotheses must be sufficiently founded and must not be multiplied without necessity. To have recourse to hypotheses without any foundation is useless and intolerable in science.

These are the rules to be observed in every scientific method. We must now study some scientific methods more in detail. For obvious reasons we will not consider the particular technical methods that are proper to particular sciences, such as the methods of arithmetic, history, chemistry, archeology, or astronomy, but limit ourselves to a study of the common scientific methods which are followed in almost any science. They are the *deductive* and *inductive* methods, and the *analytic* and *synthetic* methods. Because of the exceptional importance of scientific induction, a special chapter will be devoted to it (Ch. VIII), while two other chapters will consider the function of hypothesis and theory in science (Ch. IX) and demonstration in science (Ch. X).

I. DEDUCTION AND INDUCTION

1. *Explanation of Terms. Difference Between 'Abstractly General' and 'Collectively General'*

Best known and most important in science are the deductive and inductive methods or briefly *deduction* and *induction*. They correspond to two ways of progressing in thinking, viz., from the general and universal to the less universal or particular and individual, and from the particular and individual to the general and universal. There is little danger that the terms 'particular' and 'individual' will be misunderstood in this connection. The same, however, cannot be said regarding the terms 'general' and 'universal'; hence it will be necessary to explain briefly the exact meaning of these terms.

Abstractly General and Collectively General Notions. In dealing with general notions a distinction has to be made between 'abstractly general' or *universal* and 'collectively general' or *collective* notions. This distinction gives rise to a corresponding distinction between universal and collective judgments or propositions according as the subject of the judgment is a universal or a collective term.

Abstractly general or *universal* are all notions obtained by means of the above-mentioned total or formal abstraction. This abstraction is the reason why the notions obtained through it are truly universal and applicable to all subjects having the same specific or generic essence.

A *collective* notion, on the other hand, denotes a certain collection or multitude. This may occur in two ways:

1. The denoted multitude is considered as a whole (a so-called *unum accidentale* or 'accidental whole') in such a way that what is predicated of the whole does not necessarily apply to each of the individuals contained in it. Because such a collective notion is virtually equivalent to a singular notion, we will call it a *collectively singular* notion. Examples of this kind of notion are: the American Army, the Duquesne Basketball Team, the Lewis' Family.

2. The denoted multitude is considered as the sum total of the individuals contained in it in such a way that what is predicated of the

collective multitude applies also to each of these individuals. Because such a notion has a certain general applicability, we will call it a *collectively general* notion. Examples of this kind of notion are the subjects of the following propositions: planets move in elliptic orbits around the sun; the students in this class are more than fifteen years old; the trees of this forest are oaks.

It is to be noted that collectively general notions also result from a kind of abstraction—namely, so-called analytic abstraction (cf. Ch. III, Sect. III, 2). The individuals indicated by it can be comprehended by one term because they have something in common and are considered under this common aspect. For instance, the term 'the students in this class' unites a number of students because of their connection with this class.

Differences Between Universal and Collective Notions. There are two important differences between these two kinds of notions.

1. With respect to *contents*, a universal notion has as its content the characteristics belonging to the specific or generic essence indicated by the notion. In logic this content is called the comprehension of the notion. A collective notion, on the other hand, has as its content a concrete multitude of determinate things which retain their own individuality in the multitude. Thus the content of such a notion varies with the number of individuals it includes. In the collectively singular notion it is primarily the collection that is denoted, while the individuals are denoted only insofar as they are, or are considered to be, parts of this whole. In the collectively general notion the attention is focused primarily upon the individual and only secondarily upon the multitude.

2. With respect to *extension,* a universal notion has as its extension the sum total of all existent or possible objects represented by the notion, i.e., everything to which the comprehension of a notion can be applied in the same way. The individual things falling under the notion form a logical whole, and the common bond which makes them into a whole is their logical subordination to the notion. For this reason the extension of a universal notion is not limited to existent things but includes also all possible objects in which the notion is verified. Of the universal notion it is true that its extension increases as its comprehension decreases, and vice versa.

A collective notion, taken as such,[1] does not have extension in the same sense as a universal notion. It does not apply to an indeterminate number of objects which participate equally in a common nature expressed by the collective term. In fact, the collectively singular notion is virtually a singular notion; a family, for example, is not predicable of the father alone, the mother alone, or the children alone, but only of all of them taken together as a unit. The collectively general notion has only an apparent extension inasmuch as each member of the determinate multitude which constitutes the content of the notion can be considered separately. Such a notion is equivalent to the sum total of a determinate number of singular notions, but does not rise to the level of universality. The common bond which unites the members of a collection is not their logical subordination to the notion, but some other relation, such as that of purpose or origin. Of the collective notion it is not true that the extension increases as the comprehension decreases, and vice versa.

Universal and Collective Judgments. The extension of a judgment depends upon the extension of its subject-notion; hence it is obvious that the division of notions into universal and collective will give rise to the division of judgments into universal and collective.

The *universal* judgment has extension in the true sense of the term in accordance with the extension of its subject. It is applicable to all actual and possible objects of which the subject-notion can be predicated.

The same cannot be said of the *collective* judgment. A collectively singular judgment is virtually a singular judgment; for it can be applied only to the one whole to which the subject-notion is applicable. The collectively general judgment apparently has extension; for the judgment which can be made about the whole can be made also about its individual members. However, the reason why this is possible is not that the subject-notion expresses a common nature, but that it is a collective term indicating the individuals under one heading. The collectively general judgment is equivalent to a determinate number of singular judgments, as many as there are individuals in the collective whole. For example, "planets move in elliptic orbits around the sun" is equivalent to: "Jupiter moves in an elliptic orbit around the sun";

---

[1]We say *taken as such* because a collective notion can sometimes be universalized and thus made predicable of all similar collections; e. g., the term 'army' is a universal with respect to all existent and possible armies.

"Mars moves in an elliptic orbit around the sun"; "Venus moves in an elliptic circle around the sun"; etc.

It is to be noted that a judgment such as "all men are mortal" can be taken either as a universal judgment or as a collectively general judgment. As a universal judgment, it means "man, as man or because of his human nature, is mortal", whereas as a collective judgment it is equivalent to: "Peter is mortal; John is mortal; Mary is mortal; etc.; briefly, all men are mortal". Hence in order to avoid possible misunderstandings it would be better to use "each" instead of "all" in expressing universal judgments, or to say without adding any pronoun "man is mortal".

In a collective judgment the predicate does not denote an essential or necessary attribute of the subject; at least, the necessary character of the predicate is not enunciated as such. Its truth value consists only in the enunciation of a factual and contingent connection of subject and predicate, a connection which has been derived from experience. Scientific judgments, however, are not supposed to be mere enunciations concerning concrete and actual phenomena, but statements concerning essential relationships. Accordingly, their subjects must be universal notions endowed with a proper extension which includes all actual and possible objects having the same essential nature. Hence we may draw the conclusion that collective judgments do not play any role in the definite stage of a science, although they may be of some value in its provisional stages.

The above explanation of collective and universal terms and judgments may not appear to offer anything new to quite a few readers. However, it was necessary to clarify these notions in order to prevent possible misunderstandings about the significance and scientific value of deduction and induction.

2. *Deduction*

Description. In general the term 'deduction' indicates the intellectual operation which derives from two propositions, called 'premises', a third proposition, called 'conclusion'. Such a procedure will be legitimate only if both premises agree in one common term. For this reason it is better to describe deduction by a more detailed definition as the intellectual operation in which by means of the comparison of two terms with one and the same third (the middle term), expressed in two propositions (the premises), the agreement or disagreement of the first two terms becomes known and is expressed in a third proposition (the conclusion). When a deduction is formulated explicitly in this way, it is customary to speak of 'deductive' or 'syllogistic reasoning' or simply of 'syllogism'.

Basic Forms of Syllogism. The most used forms of deduction are symbolically represented by the following four schemes, traditionally known as *barbara, celarent, darii* and *ferio*. In these schemes S and P

$$\frac{\text{M a P}}{\text{S a M}} \qquad \frac{\text{M e P}}{\text{S a M}} \qquad \frac{\text{M a P}}{\text{S i M}} \qquad \frac{\text{M e P}}{\text{S i M}}$$
$$\text{S a P} \qquad \text{S e P} \qquad \text{S i P} \qquad \text{S o P}$$

indicate the terms that are the subject and the predicate of the conclusion, and M the middle term with which S and P are compared. The letters *a, e, i, o* respectively indicate that the proposition in question is universally affirmative, universally negative, particularly affirmative, or particularly negative. The other correct forms of syllogistic reasoning are reducible to these four basic forms.

The first proposition or 'major' of a deductive reasoning must always be universal, whether affirmative (M a P) or negative (M e P); the second or 'minor' may be universal (S a M) or particular (S i M) and even singular.

The conclusion has always the same degree of universality as the minor; hence if the minor is particular or singular, the conclusion also will be particular or singular.

Even if the minor is a universal proposition, as a rule it will be less universal than the major. For instance,

> A spirit is immortal
> The human soul is a spirit
> Therefore, the human soul is immortal

Often, especially with respect to practical applications, the minor will be a singular proposition. For example,

> The diagonals of a rhombus are perpendicular
> ABCD is a rhombus
> Therefore, the diagonals of ABCD are perpendicular

Fundamental Principles of Deduction. In general, a deduction will be a reasoning process which proceeds from the more universal to the less universal, the particular or the singular (the individual); for example, from genus to species, or from species to individual. Its most important use lies in the application of general principles and laws to subordinate classes of things and to particular cases and individual instances. This application is governed by two principles, the so-called *'dictum de omni'* and the *'dictum de nullo'*. The *'dictum de omni'* states that whatever is affirmed of a logical whole is affirmed of every part of this whole. The above-mentioned examples may be considered as applications of this principle. The *'dictum de nullo'* states that whatever is denied of a logical whole is denied of every part of this whole; for instance,

> Irrational beings are not endowed with free will
> Atoms are irrational
> Therefore, atoms are not endowed with free will

It should be clear that deduction presupposes in the human mind the possibility of philosophical abstraction, i.e. that it is possible for the mind to obtain universal notions which have an objective foundation in the things indicated by these notions. As a consequence if deduction is applied to real things, it presupposes also that the objects indicated by its notions possess a species-individual structure; otherwise the application of a universal proposition to particular cases would not make sense. For a universal statement refers to the universal (specific or generic) essence of things, and therefore by its very nature can be applied to particular cases or individual things which are individual realizations of that specific essence.

These brief remarks about deduction are sufficient for our purpose. However, care should be taken that no collective proposition be used instead of a truly universal proposition; for otherwise the result will be a mere pseudo-deduction.

3. *Pseudo-Deduction*

First Type of Pseudo-Deduction. By an apparent or pseudo-deduction we mean an activity of the human mind which starts from a collectively general proposition and applies it to a particular or individual case which is included in the collective subject of the collective proposition. In appearance this activity will be a deductive process because apparently one proceeds from the universal to the particular or individual, and this procedure is expressed in the syllogistic form used in true deduction. In reality, however, the proposition used as a major premise is a collectively general proposition, whose subject is a concrete multitude of individual cases; hence this proposition is equivalent to a number of individual judgments.

Thus the 'conclusion' predicates of an individual exactly the same thing which in the 'major' had already been predicated of it together with other individuals.

The schematic form of such a pseudo-deduction may be proposed as follows:

> A, B, C, D, . . . have the predicate P
> B is one of the individuals A, B, C, D . . .
> Therefore, B has the predicate P

For example, The boys of this class are older than fifteen years
> Peter is a boy of this class
> Therefore, Peter is older than fifteen years

There are many cases in which a collectively general proposition is applied to individual instances in the form of a syllogism, and one should be careful to distinguish such an application from a true process of scientific reasoning. The application, for instance, of criminal law to a particular case is not a truly deductive process. Let us suppose that the law states: He who steals from the U. S. Mail shall be punishable to from one to ten years in prison. We may apply this law and say: Peter Johnson stole from the U. S. Mail; and conclude that he is punishable to from one to ten years in prison. The 'major' premise is evidently a collective statement; for there is no essential or necessary connection between the crime and the punishment mentioned; the 'minor' merely states that in Johnson's case we have to do with one of the cases covered by the collective statement; hence the 'conclusion' does not teach us anything new, and the whole process does not deserve the name of deduction. It has no scientific value and should be carefully distinguished from truly deductive reasoning.

Second Type of Pseudo-Deduction. A pseudo-deduction which exhibits clearly the above-mentioned schematic form is not easily mistaken for a true deduction. However, there is another kind of pseudo-deduction, which occurs rather frequently. In this type, the 'major' is a collective proposition which is extended to a case that is not included in the collective subject but closely resembles those that are included. In other words, the 'major' is made to bear upon analogous cases. This form of pseudo-deduction may be schematized as follows:

> A, B, C, D, . . . have the predicate P
> X is similar to A, B, C, D . . .
> Therefore, X has the predicate P

This type of mental procedure occurs, for instance, if a rule obtained by a mere experience[1] in certain individual cases is extended to analogous cases that are not included in the collection of cases covered by experience. Medical experience, for example, has shown that in many cases penicillin prevents or retards the development of bacteria; and the result of this experience is now applied to new cases not studied before.

The use of this type of pseudo-deduction is very common in practical sciences, such as medicine, sociology, economy, etc., but it occurs also in theoretical sciences. In physical science, for example, there are many so-called 'laws' which are mere rules of experience or collective statements about singular cases. To give an example, atomic nuclei with an even number of protons and neutrons have a moment of momentum equal to zero. This rule has been observed in a few cases only; yet it is supposed to be generally true and is, in theoretical considerations, applied to other atomic nuclei of the same conditions.

Value of Pseudo-Deduction. While in the first type of pseudo-deduction the so-called 'conclusion' is certain and true but does not teach us anything new, in the second type of pseudo-deduction the 'conclusion' may be true or false. If it is true, it teaches us something new, but we are not certain of it because there is neither insight into the necessity of the asserted relationship nor experimental verification. If the conclusion is not true, it is obviously without any value. Since it is impossible to decide whether one has to do with the application of a collective statement which is new but uncertain or with one that is certain but not new, the 'conclusion' remains theoretically doubtful. Nevertheless it may have some practical value because it may lead to a successful practical treatment of the case under consideration.

It was necessary to insist upon the difference between true and pseudo-deduction because otherwise there would be danger that the conclusive force of a true deduction would be put on a par with that of the pseudo-deduction. The true deduction can lead to scientific knowledge, but not the pseudo-deduction, although the latter may have a certain practical value.

---

[1] The words 'rule' and 'mere experience' are used here to distinguish such a proposition from laws and principles which are based upon an insight into the essential or necessary relationship between subject and predicate. Examples of such rules are so-called statistical laws, rules of positive legislegation, etc.

Remark. According to John Stuart Mill (1806-1873) every deduction is a pseudo-deduction because, in his opinion, universal notions and universal judgments are impossible. Experience alone is the source of all knowledge, and induction is the only scientific method; hence a general statement, no matter how elementary, has no other value than a collection of singular statements about factual data. In this way, reasoning from the universal to the particular becomes impossible because there is no such thing as a universal. It would lead us too far afield to examine this theory and to show why it is wrong. The interested reader may be referred to *ex professo* studies of the matter.

4. *Induction in General. Different Kinds of Induction*

Notion of Induction. By induction in general is meant the process whereby one passes from the less universal to the more universal, or, more strictly, from the individual or particular to the general or universal. In some way or other, all our knowledge takes its beginning in sense-experience, which is knowledge of the concrete and individual; hence the inductive process is the most fundamental of all in human knowledge. According to Aristotle,[1] induction is even the only way in which man can obtain intellectual insight. It is the road which leads from the level of the sensible and the individual to the intellectual and universal. In a sense, induction is more natural for man than deduction, although deduction gives a more perfect knowledge because it starts from the universal, which has a higher degree of intelligibility.

Induction and Concepts. When the term induction is used in a very general sense for any transition from the particular to the general, it may be applied even to the formation of experiential concepts. For in these concepts, too, the experience of individual objects of the same kind finds its term in something general, viz., the universal concept. The very phantasmal images which frequently keep accompanying experiential concepts, even a long time after their acquisition, bear witness to their origin in experience. Usually, however, the intellectual process leading to the formation of universal concepts is not called induction but in general abstraction and specifically physical, mathematical, or philosophical abstraction according to the level on which the formal process terminates, i.e. according as the process

---

[1]*Post Anal.,* Bk. II, ch. 19; 100b 3 ff.

results in general concepts concerning the sense-perceptible world, mathematical concepts, or philosophical concepts.[1]

Induction and Judgments. Usually, the term 'induction' is reserved for the intellectual process which derives a general judgment from judgments concerning particular or individual complexes of data. This general judgment may have a twofold character: it may be collective (collectively general) or universal (abstractly general). As we have seen above, these two types of judgments differ in important points; hence the corresponding types of induction deserve to be treated separately.

First Type of Induction. In a collective judgment one jointly enumerates individual statements concerning particular phenomena without penetrating into the essence of things. For example, if it has been observed for each planet separately that they have a smaller density than that of the Earth, this truth may be expressed in the statement: all planets other than the Earth have a smaller density than that of the Earth. Such a statement has no other value than any other collection: it is an easy way of summing up in one statement many individual statements.

The enumeration leading to a collective statement may extend to all the individual cases in which a certain predicate is found to be truthfully predicable of its subject or not. If it extends to all, the induction will be called *complete induction* or rather *induction by complete enumeration.* If the enumeration does not cover all cases, but the collective judgment is extended to non-observed cases in the belief that they, too, have the same character, the process of induction is *incomplete but completed by analogy.* In the most favorable case all individual instances, both observed and non-observed, will have the same character, and the value of such an inductive process is equal to that of complete induction. For instance, after observing that the orbit of Mars was an ellipse, Kepler concluded that the orbits of all planets are ellipses; this conclusion was later shown to be true. Frequently, however, there will be exceptions, so that the collective judgment is merely a rule that applies most of the time. To give a few examples,

Metals are heavier than water. Exceptions: lithium, potassium, sodium.

---

[1]See above, Chapter III, Sect. IV.

> Gases, liquids, and solids expand when heated. There are many
> exceptions; such as water in the temperature region of 0—4
> Centigrades.
> The volume of a body increases in melting and decreases in solidi-
> fying. Well-known exceptions are iron, silver, and bismuth.

The collectively general judgments obtained by such inductive
processes are sometimes used as the 'major premises' in pseudo-deduction, as we have seen above in this chapter.

Second Type of Induction. Very often it will be possible to conclude from the observation of individual and particular instances of
the same kind to the abstractly general or universal, from the individual to the species or genus, so that truly universal concepts and
judgments are formed. This possibility will arise if the particular
observations point to qualities which have an essential or necessary
character, so that they must be present in all objects having the same
essence, i.e., in all objects denoted by one and the same abstract
concept or belonging to the same logical whole. In such a case it
will be possible to make a statement concerning this essence which
is truly universal.

The possibility of such a procedure enables us to arrive at general
statements about necessary and essential qualities and to discover
scientific laws. In this kind of induction there is no necessity to
observe all the individual instances of a certain nature—it would not
be possible anyhow—all that is needed is sufficient observation to
penetrate into the essence of the observed phenomenon. Sometimes
one instance may be sufficient for this purpose; e.g. from any individual triangle or parallelogram a mathematician is able to deduce the
essential qualities proper to a triangle or parallelogram in general.
Generally, however, a single observation is not sufficient. Later, in
Chapter VIII, we shall see how it is possible to distinguish essential
qualities from contingent ones in the data of the senses.

Because no complete observation of all instances is necessary, this
kind of induction is called *incomplete induction*. It is also known as
scientific induction because it leads to truly scientific statements and
laws.

Because of the exceptional importance of scientific induction in
the study of the sciences, and especially because of the difficulties
arising in its philosophical foundation, a special chapter will be
devoted to this method. The discussion that follows here therefore

will be restricted to complete induction and by-analogy-completed induction.

5. *Complete Induction and by-Analogy-Completed Induction*

Complete Induction or Induction by Complete Enumeration. As we have seen in the foregoing, complete induction results only in the recording of a number of individual statements in a collective statement. Individual things or phenomena of the same kind are considered under a certain aspect by means of an analytic abstraction. The resulting statement is a collectively general statement, equivalent to a determinate number of individual experiential statements.

Such a collective statement may have certain practical advantages, inasmuch as its simplicity renders it easier to handle the multitude. There is no question, however, of real progress in knowledge, of a transition from the known to the unknown. The collective statement does not give us a better insight into the nature of the objects considered than any of the individual statements; it never rises to the level of the universal statement. Complete induction establishes merely what *is* in fact, but it does not establish that or why it *must* be so. It does not arrive at the reason underlying the relationship between subject and predicate expressed in the collective statement, because it merely records the observation of sense experience, which can never reveal the essence of the things observed.

For this reason complete induction does not rise to the level of truly scientific knowledge and does not lead to an insight into the phenomena under investigation, because it does not give knowledge of the causes of these phenomena.

The analytic abstraction upon which it is based merely classifies objects according to their characteristics in accordance with the methods used in their observation or a certain pre-established purpose. Contrary to total and formal abstraction, it is not able to judge about the necessity or contingency of these characteristics.

Even if all individuals of a collection show the same characteristics, one is not justified in concluding that these characteristics are necessary in the sense that they find their origin in the essential structure of these individuals. For example, in all mammals one can find traces of hair, yet this characteristic certainly does not flow from the nature of mammal, which implies merely that the female suckle their young.

A priori speaking, it is possible for a contingent quality to be present in all cases because of certain permanently present external circumstances; for instance, weight is found in all bodies because of their permanent presence in a gravitational field. However, the regular occurrence or permanence of certain qualities may indicate that there is a basis for them in the essence of the objects considered; and in such a case this essential basis remains to be investigated.

By-Analogy-Completed Induction. Generally it is not possible to investigate all individual instances of a group of phenomena or objects. In such cases a large number of cases are investigated, and the result of the investigation is laid down in a rule. This rule is then extended to unobserved instances of the same group because of their similarity or analogy to the observed cases, in virtue of the principle of analogy: "analogous phenomena usually have analogous causes, effects, and properties".

This type of induction is used very frequently in daily life. What is observed in many instances is generalized as a rule supposed to be valid in all cases. But it is made use of also in scientific investigations, at least on a provisional basis, when it is not possible to obtain certainty about the essential character of a suspected relationship by means of scientific induction. As examples we may point to Lavoisier's law of the conservation of weight, at least at the time of its discovery, and Proust's law of constant composition.

The value of such a process of induction is, in the most favorable case, equal to that of complete induction. In such a case, the resulting statement is a collectively general statement and stands for a multitude of singular statements. There is no question of real progress in knowledge, of a transition from the known to the unknown. With respect to the observed instances the general collective statement is true and certain, but with respect to the unobserved instances it has been extrapolated and therefore can be either true or false. Hence with regard to these unobserved instances it has only a certain probability, although it may be used for practical purposes.

Scientific and Practical Value of Complete and by-Analogy-Completed Induction. Although complete induction does not lead to new knowledge, and induction completed by analogy at most leads to uncertain or probable knowledge, nevertheless they often have great value for science and for practical purposes.

With respect to *science,* they are valuable for the organization and classification of scientific data because they make possible a quick survey of observed data; e.g. in such sciences as linguistics, descriptive sociology, ethnology, medicine, etc. For example, they can provide the necessary data for the investigation of the relationship between the occurrence of certain diseases and climate, region, age, general health, habits of living and working, income, ethnic background, atmospheric conditions, sun spots, etc. The gathering and classification of such data can lead to the discovery of a regular connection between certain data and consequently to the discovery of an essential or necessary relationship.

With respect to *practical purposes,* they have value, especially in the field of practical and normative sciences, such as ethics, law, normative sociology and economy, medicine, etc. For example, statistical rules concerning the behavior of man under certain conditions, or the occurrence and course of certain diseases, may lead to the formulation of definite rules of conduct. If, for instance, observation shows that bad housing conditions give rise to an increase in immorality, it becomes imperative to establish good housing conditions; if certain mineral springs are observed to have a beneficial influence upon a given disease, a visit to these springs can be recommended to sufferers of this disease.

In this way, rules established by means of induction completed by analogy offer a possibility of practical applications in other similar instances. However, such applications are hypothetical in nature and do not rise above a greater or lesser degree of probability. Every new concrete instance to which the rule is applied may deviate from the established rule. For example, the course taken by a concrete case of illness may differ from the general rule established by experience.

If the application of such a general rule of experience to a concrete instance is considered as a transition from the general to the particular, one has to do with what we have called above (No. 3) a pseudo-deduction.

6. *Schema of Deduction and Induction*

We will conclude this discussion of deduction and induction by giving in schematic form a survey of the various forms of deduction and induction.

DEDUCTION			INDUCTION		
from the general to the less general, particular, or individual			from the less general, particular, or individual to the general		
pseudo-deduction		*genuine deduction*	*non-scientific induction*		*scientific induction*
proceeds from the collectively general to the particular or individual		proceeds from the abstractly general to the particular or individual	proceeds from the particular or individual to the collectively general		proceeds from the particular or individual to the abstractly general
the 'major' is a collective judgment		the 'major' is a universal judgment, which applies to all actual and possible cases	*first type* complete induction (induction by complete enumeration)	*second type* incomplete induction completed by analogy	incomplete induction
first type the 'conclusion' is a particular judgment explicitly included in the 'major'	*second type* the 'conclusion' is a particular judgment to which the 'major' is extended because of a certain analogy	the conclusion is an application of the universal major to one of the particular cases falling under its extension	the 'conclusion' refers to a collective whole results in rules applicable to a collective whole		the conclusion refers to a logical whole results in laws and universal propositions concerning essential relations
may have some practical value		has a truly scientific value	may have some practical value		has a truly scientific value

II. ANALYTIC AND SYNTHETIC METHODS. A POSTERIORI AND A PRIORI METHODS

Apart from the inductive and deductive methods, which play the most important role in the methodology of the sciences, there are other methods which deserve our attention—namely, the analytic and synthetic methods, and the *a posteriori* and *a priori* methods. The terms 'analytic' and 'synthetic' point to the manner in which one proceeds, i.e. whether analysis or synthesis is predominant in a scientific procedure. The terms '*a posteriori*' and '*a priori*' on the other hand, indicate whether the known datum which serves as the starting point of the scientific process is prior or posterior in the order of reality to the unknown of which knowledge is sought. Of course, the terms 'prior' and 'posterior' should not be understood here as referring to time, but to priority or posteriority of nature. As we will see in the course of this section, the analytic method partly coincides with the *a posteriori* method, and the synthetic method does the same with respect to the *a priori* method. In such a case the method used will be analytic and *a posteriori* or synthetic and *a priori*.

1. *Analytic and A Posteriori Methods*

If the known datum is posterior in the order of nature to the unknown of which knowledge is sought, one will have to proceed regressively or *a posteriori*. Thus one proceeds against the natural order of things: from the particular or more determinate to the general or less determinate; from the concrete to the abstract; from the complex or composite to the simple or to constituent elements; from the properties of things to their nature; from effect to cause; from conclusion to principles; from applications to the thesis.

In this method the known datum will be stripped of its complex structure; the composite or the complex will be resolved into its component simple elements; the abstract will be separated from the concrete; etc. Hence it is clear why this method is called *analysis* (from the Greek verb '*analyein*', to dissolve, to separate).

Analysis may be either real or logical. In *real* analysis a real object is decomposed into its heterogeneous parts, and the connection of these parts with one another and with the whole is determined. In *logical* or intellectual analysis a concept or statement is resolved into more simple concepts or general principles so that there will be a transition from the particular to the general; e.g. in an inductive process. In both cases the result will be obtained by analysis.

With regard to the names of the method, if emphasis is given to the regressive aspect of the procedure from what is posterior in the order of nature to what is prior, it will be called an *a posteriori* method; if, however, the analytic aspect is more emphasized, it will be called an *analytic* method. Although in many cases the analytic character will perhaps be more obvious, the *a posteriori* character is more profound. Moreover, it is to be noted that the term '*a posteriori*' is more general than the term 'analytic.' For not every *a posteriori* procedure arrives at something more simple by means of an analysis of the more complex. For instance, the cause reached by an *a posteriori* method may be more complex than the actual effect.

With respect to the means of demonstration used in this method, it will be sufficient to point out that it uses induction and deductive *a posteriori* demonstration.

2. *Synthetic and A Priori Methods*

If the known datum which serves as the starting point of the process is prior in the order of nature to the unknown of which knowledge is sought, one has to proceed progressively or *a priori*. In this case, one proceeds in accordance with the natural order of things: from the general or less determinate to the particular or more determinate, e.g. from species to individual; from the abstract to the concrete; from the simple to the complex; from elements to the composite; from a nature to its properties; from cause to effect; from principle to conclusion; from a thesis to its application, from law to fact.

In this method known elements will be combined into a composite whole; abstract data will be put together into a concrete combination; principles will be joined to reach a conclusion; etc. Hence it is clear why this method is called *synthesis* (from the Greek verb '*syntithenai*', to put together).

Like analysis, synthesis may be real or logical. It is *real* if real component parts are united into a real whole, as building blocks into a structure. It is *logical* or intellectual if a complex notion or a connected system of theses is constructed from general concepts or principles or if parts are arranged according to the logical whole to which they belong. In both cases, the result will always be a kind of composition or synthesis of something less determinate with other more specific elements.

With regard to the names of the method, it is called '*a priori*' because of the progressive procedure from what is prior in the order of nature to what is posterior, and 'synthetic' because of the composition or synthesis which this procedure implies. According as the first or the second characteristic reveals itself more clearly, preference is given to the first or the second name. The *a priori* character is more profound, but the synthetic feature may sometimes reveal itself more clearly. Here, again, it is to be noted that the term '*a priori* method' is wider in meaning than 'synthetic method.' For not every procedure *a priori* is necessarily synthetic; e.g., that from cause to effect, or that from nature to property.

The demonstrative means used in this method is the deductive *a priori* demonstration.

3. *The Connection Between Analysis and Synthesis on the one Hand, and Induction and Deduction on the Other*

Every *induction* is analytic, for it obtains its results by means of the analysis of the complex data of experience. Induction proceeds regressively, starting from what is ontologically posterior. *Deduction,* on the other hand, is synthetic, for it reaches its results by means of composition. In a deductive argument the conclusion is reached by the combination of two general propositions or of one general proposition and an experiential judgment. Deduction is usually also progressive because in general it proceeds from what is ontologically prior; e.g. from species to individual. However, there are also deductions which, at least in part, proceed from what is ontologically posterior; e.g. the proofs for the existence of God from the existence of contingent beings by means of the principle of causality. In mathematics, too, there are many *a posteriori* deductions; e. g., if one proves that a figure constructed in a determinate way is a parallelogram or a triangle. Nevertheless, such an *a posteriori* deduction remains synthetic. The reverse, however, is not true. Not every analysis is an induction, and not every synthesis is a deduction. The concept 'analysis' comprises more than purely scientific induction, for it applies also to the abstractive formation of concepts, *a posteriori* deduction, and real analysis. 'Synthesis', in turn, comprises more than mere deduction, for it applies also to the formation of a judgment and to real synthesis.

4. *Combination of Methods: Deductive-Inductive, Analytico-Synthetic Methods*

No science is exclusively deductive or inductive, analytic or synthetic. Nevertheless, it is quite possible for a science to be predominantly deductive or predominantly inductive. For instance, mathematics is predominantly deductive, for it usually proceeds from the general to the particular, and views a particular problem as an instance of a more general problem. Even if a mathematician arrives at a particular thesis without deduction, he will never be satisfied before he has been able to deduce it from more general theses, which in turn are based upon fundamental mathematical principles. Nevertheless, even in mathematics, it will frequently happen that recourse must be made to induction, especially when hitherto unexplored problems demand a solution.[1] On the other hand, a science can be predominantly inductive, as is exemplified by the experiential sciences, especially physical science. But even in physical sciences deduction has to be used if particular phenomena are to be explained from a broader point of view, or if particular laws have to be derived from more general ones. Hence the theoretical sections of these sciences, such as theoretical physics, are predominantly deductive.

Deduction is, as we have seen, a kind of synthesis, and induction a kind of analysis. Hence the combination of induction with deduction is at the same time a combination of analysis with synthesis. For human sciences as a whole, the analytico-synthetic method is the only true method. Especially in the experiential sciences man has to start from the data of internal and external sense experience. Facts and particular data have to be analyzed in order to reach knowledge of the general or to proceed from effect to cause. Next, the knowledge acquired in this manner has to be applied to particular cases by deduction, and general concepts, principles and laws have to be used synthetically to obtain an insight into complex reality. In other sciences, too, such as mathematics and philosophy, one has to proceed analytically and synthetically. With respect to mathematics, this is clear from what has been said about its use of deduction and induction. Moreover, the first mathematical concepts, such as number, point, and line, are obtained by abstraction and therefore analytically. The same is true of certain axioms, such as the funda-

---

[1] Cf. P. Henry van Laer, *Philosophico-Scientific Problems* (*Duquesne Studies, Philosophical Series,* vol. 3), Pittsburgh 1953, Ch. VII; also Part II of this book.

mental axioms of Euclidean geometry.   Philosophy also combines analysis with synthesis.   For instance, in theodicy, one first ascends from the world to God as its first cause, and then endeavors to derive from this knowledge of God a better insight into the relationship between God and creatures; in psychology, a study of the activity of intellect and will leads to an insight into the nature of intellect and will, and this knowledge, in turn, is used to obtain a better insight into the nature of free acts of will.

5. *Some Remarks Concerning the Use of Analysis and Synthesis*

In general, we may say that in scientific endeavors the analytic method is used to obtain an insight into the complexity of the data of experience and thus to arrive at truth.   The synthetic method, on the other hand, is used to construct a coherent system, called a science, in which the particular is assigned a place in the light of the general.

The synthetic method is more suitable for a didactic exposé, which aims at the clarification of the particular by means of the general. Sometimes, however, the analytic method is didactically preferable— namely, if it is desirable to show how a certain truth has been discovered, as for instance, in an historical study of physical science.

Besides, the preponderance given to either analysis or synthesis may be a question of individual preference.   Certain minds are more inclined to analysis: they apply themselves to the accurate observation and resolution of complex data; they have what Pascal has called *l'esprit de finesse*.   Others are more synthetically inclined: they like to construct systems in which the particular is seen and explained from the general; theirs is *l'esprit de géométrie*.

CHAPTER EIGHT

INCOMPLETE OR SCIENTIFIC INDUCTION[1]

INTRODUCTION

Just as the other types of induction, scientific induction is a transition from the particular to the general. But while complete induction and by-analogy-completed induction imply a transition from the particular to the collectively general, scientific induction is a transition from the particular to the abstractly general or universal. The judgment resulting from a process of scientific induction purports to be a judgment concerning essential qualities and necessary or essential relationships between phenomena.

Thus scientific induction amounts to this that after sufficient observation and critical examination of individual instances, subject to sense experience, a conclusion is drawn regarding the necessary or essential relationship between certain data of observation. This conclusion is expressed in a proposition whose typical formulas are as follows:

Property B is necessarily or essentially connected with subject A.

Phenomenon B is necessarily or essentially connected with phenomenon A.

A is the cause of B.

B is the effect of A.

In these formulas A and B do not stand for individual instances, but indicate something specific. In many cases propositions such as these formulas are called 'laws' or 'natural laws'.

In opposition to the complete induction discussed in the preceding chapter, scientific induction is called *incomplete,* because not all the individual instances of a phenomenon are investigated. Such an investigation would not even be possible, because scientific induction is not concerned with a definite collection, but with an abstract or logical whole, of which the individual instances are logical inferiors.

In the respect of incompleteness it resembles the above-described incomplete induction which is completed by analogy. However, there

---

[1]Most of the contents of this chapter has been previously published in Dutch under the title "Wijsgerige aspecten van de wetenschappelijke inductie", *Tijdschrift voor Philosophie,* vol. 16 (1954), pp. 55-84.

is also a very important difference. In by-analogy-completed induction a rule established by experience regarding a limited number of instances is extended to others because of their analogous resemblance. But in scientific induction a universal conclusion is drawn from a critical examination of a limited number of instances because this examination has given an intellectual insight into the nature of the phenomenon under investigation.

This type of induction is called *scientific* because it gives a scientific insight, i.e. a certain insight into the nature or essence of the object considered. Scientific induction is the basic method of investigation in experiential sciences, especially physical sciences. Of the two terms 'scientific' and 'incomplete' induction, the former is preferable because the term 'incomplete' applies also to what we have called above 'by-analogy-completed induction'; thus the use of the same name for both types could become an occasion for confusion.

Remark. It is to be noted that for an empiristically-minded scientist there is no difference between by-analogy-completed induction and scientific induction. According to empiricism, our knowledge can never rise above the data of experience so that true knowledge of essences is impossible. A realistically-minded scientist, however, accepts—and justly so—that our intellect is capable of deriving certain knowledge of essences from the data of sense experience; hence for him there is a great difference between these two types of induction. But he, too, is convinced that in practice it will often be difficult to arrive at essential knowledge and that one cannot always exclude the possibility of mistakes in this matter. Thus it may happen that what apparently is a true scientific induction is in reality nothing but by-analogy-completed induction. This possibility of mistaking one type of induction for the other is an added reason why it is important to realize their difference so as to be on guard against the dangers inherent in induction. We will have an opportunity to revert to this question in a later part of this study.

I. THE PROPER CHARACTER OF SCIENTIFIC INDUCTION

A Difficulty. At first sight, scientific induction makes a rather strange impression. How is it possible to make the transition from the sense experience of individual instances which exhibit a certain regularity to a universal conclusion which asserts a necessary or essential relationship? One cannot, without any further justification, make the leap from a number of similar individual instances to every instance and a universal judgment. Not even the examination of very many instances would justify such a procedure. Hence even in the most favorable case so-called scientific induction would not amount to more than by-analogy-completed induction, and therefore, with respect to unobserved instances, it could not offer more than a certain probability and a basis for a psychological conviction that the rule is likely to apply to all instances. As a matter of fact, Hume and the empiricists take this viewpoint of scientific induction.

A Spontaneous Conviction. Whether he is realistically-minded or not, in practice every scientist will frequently and, as it were, intuitively pass from the observation of a regular connection between two phenomena in a number of individual instances to a conclusion which is considered (or at least treated) as a proposition that expresses a necessary connection and therefore is applicable to new unobserved instances. Yet such an application is legitimate only if the proposition is really of a universal nature.

It is evident that this situation raises an important problem. If the conclusion is really of a universal nature, in the sense explained above (Ch. III, Sect. II, 3 and III, 4; Ch. VII, Sect. I, 1), its foundation will have to be more than mere sense experience. The very certainty of the conviction with which such a universal conclusion is drawn is a sign that in such a process one has to do with a conscious or unconscious application of general principles that form part and parcel of the human mind, and that these principles are sufficiently clear not to cause any difficulty in their application to a particular case. If this is so, scientific induction will find its justification in a logical *deduction,* and this logical deduction will explain why man is convinced that he has a true insight into the nature of the object under consideration and that his procedure is legitimate. For only deduction is able to give such an insight into the necessity of the conclusion.

Objective Foundation of This Conviction. It is the task of the philosophy of science to find the hidden foundation of scientific induction and to disclose the general insights and principles upon which man relies, as it were, intuitively in their concrete applications.

The deductive process which justifies the process of inductive reasoning is easy enough to find. We may formulate it as follows:

Major: Whatever happens with *regularity,* i.e. without exception, in the material world happens of necessity.

Minor: An investigation of the data of experience shows that a phenomenon of species A is *regularly* accompanied by a phenomenon of species B.

Conclusion: Therefore, a phenomenon of species A is necessarily connected with a phenomenon of species B.

In case the minor is formulated differently, the conclusion may be: property A belongs of necessity to subject B, or phenomenon B is the effect of cause A. In all cases the conclusion expresses something specific and essential; it is a genuine abstractly general statement, which therefore can be applied to individual instances.

This process is a true deduction, at least if the major premise is a universal proposition, which we will have to investigate later in this chapter. The minor is the result of a scientific inductive investigation, which has to be performed in accordance with the methods of the sciences concerned. Because of this minor the whole process itself is called inductive reasoning or induction, for it is an intellectual analysis of observed individual facts which leads to a conclusion concerning the necessary relationship between phenomenon A and B.

Of course, the fact that the inductive process of thought uses *de facto* general principles and that this process can be represented explicitly in a deductive syllogism, does not obliterate the essential difference between induction and deduction. For it remains true that, contrary to deduction, induction starts from the concrete and individual and leads to an abstractly general statement. However, this process of thought is justified only if, consciously or unconsciously, it is based upon general principles which express intellectual intuitions. To make these intuitions explicit it is good to start from the above-mentioned deduction and then to search for the foundations on which the major and minor are based. Again it is the philosophy of science which has the task of finding the basic insights and principles of which the major is an application and showing that the investigation of individual instances can lead to the conclusion about regularity which constitutes the minor premise of the above-mentioned deductive process. The foundation of the major will be found in the realm of general philosophy or metaphysics—namely, in the principle of regularity. The foundation of the minor will have to be sought in a critical analysis of the method followed in the scientific investigation of the data of experience. In the course of this analysis it will become clear that this scientific examination is based upon various presuppositions which can be justified only by philosophy. The subsequent section of this chapter will be devoted to a study of these foundations.

II. CRITICAL EXAMINATION OF THE FOUNDATION OF SCIENTIFIC INDUCTION

In the examination of the foundation of scientific induction it is necessary to distinguish the foundations that still belong to the sphere of the special sciences, such as the physical sciences, from the foundations that must be presupposed by these sciences. We will call the former the *immediate* foundations, and the latter the *ultimate* foundations. Evidently, the examination and justification of the foundations that are presupposed by the special sciences lie outside the sphere of these sciences and therefore belong to the realm of philosophy.

1. *Immediate Foundation*

The starting point of scientific induction lies in the observation of some or, if need be, many instances which are judged to be of the same kind in a definite respect. Accordingly, in general the interest is not focused on the individual instances for their own sake, but only insofar as they may be considered to represent a species. For the purpose is to arrive at a universal statement regarding the specific nature of things. For this purpose it is not sufficient to have at one's disposal a number of isolated judgments regarding observed singular things. The observations or possibly the experiments will have to be arranged in such a way that it will be possible to distinguish the specific properties from the individual determinations, and to discover, moreover, a regular connection. The general method used by the physical sciences may be briefly described as follows.

General Method of the Physical Sciences. 1. In the first place, the observed instances must not be considered separately, but brought into a mutual relationship with one another and with other instances of the same kind observed in different places and at different times. Sometimes they are compared also with instances of a different kind with which they share certain characteristics, so that it is possible to arrive at a more valuable appreciation of the importance to be attached to their resemblance and dissimilarity.

Thus the observed data are considered against a certain background of experimental data. For this reason it may happen that even a single careful observation can lead to the discovery of an essential connection. For example, a single careful determination of the boiling point of a pure substance can be sufficient to speak of *the* boiling point of the matter in question, for relying upon previous experimental data one can know that a pure substance possesses clearly determined physical and chemical qualities, which therefore are called 'constants'. The boiling and melting points are examples of such 'constants'.

2. Secondly, the mere fact that certain phenomena can be observed repeatedly with respect to the same or similar kinds of matter is not sufficient to warrant a conclusion concerning their necessary relationship. It is essential that in addition the comparison of the various observed instances reveal characteristic *regularity* or, in the case of experiments, 'reproducibility'. By regularity or 'reproducibility' we mean that a definite quality is found in subjects of a definite kind without any exception, or that two phenomena accompany each other without exception, even if their circumstances are varied.

3. Frequently, a large number of protracted and varied investigations are needed to find a certain regularity and isolate it from the complex whole of phenomena with which it occurs in nature. The methods used in these investigations are not always the same. Some of them were described by Francis Bacon (1561-1626) in his Novum Organum under the titles *tabula praesentiae, tabula absentiae,* and *tabula graduum.* A better formulation was given by John Stuart Mill (1806-1873) in his work A System of Logic. He enumerates the methods of agreement, of difference, of residues, and of concomitant variations. However, it is beyond the scope of this study to enter into details concerning these methods. The interested reader may be referred to textbooks of logic or of the methodology of science, which generally devote a few pages to them.[2] But in Section Six of this chapter we will indicate the general principles upon which these methods are based.

2. *Ultimate Foundation*

As should be clear from the foregoing discussion, the immediate foundations allow a conclusion to be drawn regarding the regularity of a connection, but they cannot explain man's intuitive conviction that the thought process of scientific induction is legitimate and that

---

[2]See, e.g. S. Mellone, *Introductory Textbook of Logic,* Edinburgh 19th ed., 1937, Ch. IX.

the general conclusions resulting from it are certain. For a closer inspection will raise a number of questions which still remain to be answered. These questions are the following.

1. Why is it legitimate to draw from the observation of individual cases a conclusion concerning a species? Such a procedure appears to suppose that, apart from individual characteristics, things possess also specific properties, i.e. that there is a species-individual structure in material things.

2. What is the reason why it is legitimate to combine experiential data, which often have been obtained at different times and places, in order to arrive at a general statement concerning a definite species of things or phenomena?

3. What is the foundation of the special methods of investigation used to discover the regular connections?

4. What is the reason why from the regular connection of phenomena one may conclude to a necessary connection or essential relationship, or in other words, what is the foundation of the principle of regularity?

These questions give rise to several philosophic considerations, which shall be briefly considered in the subsequent sections in the following order:

The meaning and foundation of the principle of regularity (Section III) ;

The species-individual structure of material things (Section IV) ;

Problems concerning the combination of experiential data (Section V) ;

The foundation of the special methods of investigation (Section VI).

III. THE MEANING AND FOUNDATION OF THE PRINCIPLE OF REGULARITY

1. *Meaning and Foundation of Regularity*

The Concept of Regularity. Everyone who is *ex professo* engaged in the physical sciences looks for regularity, i.e. for the occurrence without any exception of a certain connection between phenomena, or between subjects and certain properties, etc. Upon the basis of this regularity he does not hesitate to draw a conclusion about their necessary connection. Apparently he sees, as it were, intuitively that a regular connection in material nature is also a necessary connection. In other words, he makes intuitively use of the principle that regularity in material nature is based upon the essence of things.

It is clear that this principle is not one for which the physical sciences themselves are able to supply the justification; hence it is a presupposition of these sciences. This presupposition, moreover, is essential to them in the sense that the value of scientific investigation stands or falls with it. Implicitly assumed in physical science, it is made explicit by the philosophy of science. Its foundation, again, will have to be supplied by philosophy.

The concept of *regularity* is meaningful only if there is question of two or more things or phenomena which accompany one another. For regularity means the regular connection of two or more phenomena of things. There will be question of regularity if things of kind A always have quality B; or if a phenomenon of the kind A is always accompanied by a phenomenon of the kind B; briefly, if A is connected with B in all individual instances, regardless of the concrete circumstances of time, place, surroundings, and influences. Such a regular connection will have to be discovered by the observation of a greater or lesser number of individual instances which either occur independently of our influence or are experimentally produced by our activities. If the latter is the case, one may speak of 'reproducibility' instead of regularity.

The opposite of regular connection is random connection or rather contingent connection. By a contingent connection is meant that the connection between A and B is unstable and accidental: sometimes they are together, at other times they do not occur together. Hence, regularity and contingency with respect to the same are mutually exclusive.

Foundation of Regularity. No event, change, property, or activity in nature finds the sufficient reason for its being in itself, but only in something else. In one way or another, each of them is caused, the term 'caused' being taken here in a broader sense so as to include all manners of causality. Hence the regular connection of the phenomena A and B in nature will find its foundation in the regular or constant presence of similar causal influences. In general, therefore, the principle of sufficient reason, or rather the principle of causality, will enable the observer to conclude to similarity of causal influences if a regular connection of A and B is observed. This conclusion may be expressed in the formula: "every regular connection demands for the cases concerned similarity of causal influences". We will call this formula the *general principle of regularity*.

It should be obvious that these causal influences can give rise to the connection of A and B in different ways. For example, A can be the formal or material cause of B, as when B is a property of A; or A can be the efficient cause of B; or A and B both can be caused by one and the same causal factor; etc. The principle of regularity does not specify anything about the nature of the causal influence, but merely indicates that a regular connection of A and B must be based upon similar causal influences.

2. *Regularity and Free Causes*

The regular connection of two events requires similarity of foundation or causes, but not that these causes operate of necessity. Even non-necessary or free causes can give rise to a regularly recurrent event. For example, it is possible that someone will always rise at the same time of the day or pass a certain street corner at exactly the same time. A well-known example was Kant, whose regularity was so perfect that people were able to set their watches as he passed their homes. In such cases there is a regular connection between a definite time and a definite event; yet not even after observing such a connection for a lifetime would one dare to conclude to an inner necessity. At most, one could conclude to an extrinsic necessity, to disciplinary forces or command; for example, in the regularity shown in boarding schools.

Even in such cases regularity is not a mere coincidence. It has a foundation, which is to be found in the free will of the individuals who regulate their behavior by definite motives. Hence here, too, there is a constancy of causes or a constant recurrence of similar causes, but no intrinsic necessity. The regularity is caused by the free decisions of man who regulates a certain activity in such a way that a similar relationship recurs constantly.

3. *Regularity and Necessary Causes*

From the foregoing it should be clear that from a regular connection one cannot conclude immediately to a necessary connection, i.e., to a connection which cannot be different because of the intrinsic necessity of the causal influences involved. Nevertheless, it is a general conviction of man that such a conclusion is legitimate with respect to phenomena of material nature. This conviction can find its basis only in an insight that is implicitly assumed when such a conclusion is drawn. It is our task to make this insight explicit.

When there is question of regularity in the free activity of man nobody dares to conclude to an inner necessity. On the other hand, there is no hesitation with respect to events that belong to material nature. Hence the difference must spring from the difference in nature of the causes that are at work in free activity and natural events. A simple intellectual insight teaches us that in the case of material nature we have to do with causes which work of necessity of nature, i.e., with causes which cannot not work or work in any other way than they actually do. Such causes cannot take a free decision concerning the time, nature, and intensity of their activity. Thus the phenomena of material nature proceed of necessity from the operation of causes which by their very nature are determined to a definite activity. In this way we see that the above-mentioned conclusion from regularity to necessity is based upon the insight of the determinism of nature.

Where causes are at work which operate of necessity of nature, i.e. where one has to do with a deterministic system, it will be possible to conclude from a regular connection to a necessary connection, to a connection which is consequent upon the essence of things and therefore occurs of necessity and invariably in all individual instances of the same kind. Thus we arrive at the formulation of the principle of regularity with respect to material nature: *whatever happens regularly in material nature happens of necessity* (i.e. because of the nature or essence of material things), or: *in material nature a regular connection is a necessary or essential connection.*

4. *Regularity and Probability*

In the preceding pages there has been question of regular relationships, caused freely or by necessity of nature, between individual phenomena of kind A and individual phenomena of kind B. It is possible that what is considered to be an individual phenomenon is in reality the result of the co-operation of a large group of individual factors. In such a case the regular occurrence of the phenomenon is based upon a hitherto unmentioned kind of regularity which sometimes occurs when there are large numbers of individuals of the same kind. Usually this regularity will consist in this that in equal periods of time an equal percentage of individuals belonging to the same group will act in the same manner or undergo action in the same manner. Let us give a few examples. In a large group of population there will be each year approximately the same number of suicides, marriages, deaths at the same age from the same disease, etc. In a large number of radioactive atoms of the same kind the same percentage will disintegrate during equal periods of time. If a die is cast many times, the same number will be obtained in approximately one sixth of the total number of casts. With respect to individual instances (persons, atoms, casts) it is impossible to make any prediction about the occurrence of such events. In the case of free human activities this impossibility is based upon the fact that the event is not determined by nature; and in the case of naturally determined events prediction is impossible because our knowledge of the causal factors involved is insufficient. For this reason there can be no question of certainty but only of probability.

The regularity in events of this kind is *different in nature* from the regularities mentioned above. In cases involving the activity of free causes, there is no tendency to regularity: no one will be going to commit suicide just to make sure that the average number of suicides is going to be reached. In cases involving causes which work of necessity, such as radioactive atoms, there does not seem to be any simple inner determination to disintegrate; for otherwise all atoms would do it in the same way. Hence the question must be raised how such regularity can be explained.

In all these cases, whether free will is involved or not, the phenomena in question are very *complex*. Many causes are present and concur to produce the result. Where man's free will plays a role, as in suicide, there are many determining factors: e.g., the individual's psychical disposition, which is determined by his natural inclination and surroundings; environmental factors and events in life which are interpreted in a characteristically individual way; finally a complex struggle of motives in the free choice of the will. Where free will plays no part, as in the case of death from tuberculosis, there is a certain hereditary predisposition, a danger of infection which depends upon surroundings, climate, hygiene, etc., individual resistance which depends upon physical and psychical factors, nourishment, care, etc. Thus there are numerous causal factors which exercise a positive or negative influence upon the incurrence and development of the disease. In the case of a die, the result depends upon numerous factors which influence the individual casts; e.g., the motion and position of the hand at the moment the die is cast, the resistance of the air, the reaction of the part of the table on which the die makes contact with its surface, etc. In the case of radioactive atoms, there are the inner condition of the complex structure of the atom and external influences, such as collision, repulsion, mutual contact, and the action of electric, magnetic, electromagetic and gravitational fields.

Although in all these and similar examples there can be a great difference with respect to individual cases, nevertheless in a large number of individual cases a certain *average* will result because of the levelling influence by which certain causal factors neutralize one another either partially or completely. This average will be about the same for equal, sufficiently long periods of time, and as a result there seems to be a regular connection between a definite lapse of time and the occurrence of the events. The problem of regularity and probability contains other aspects which would need to be considered in a complete study of the problem. But the explanations given above are sufficient for our purpose. However, one remark needs to be added. It is said rather frequently that there is *indeterminism* in these cases insofar as individuals are concerned. A distinction has to be made. In cases where the result depends ultimately upon an act of *free will,* there are many causal factors which operate of necessity, but there is also a non-determined factor, namely, the free choice of the will. However, even this factor is not an absolutely arbitrary element, but a self-determination which is based upon motives. These motives can be very numerous and contrary to one another. Hence, although the final decision of the will is free, there are many determining factors which contribute to this decision. On the other hand, in cases where all causal factors are of a *purely material* nature, there can be no question of self-determination. In any individual case the final result is totally determined, partly by the inner dynamic structure of the object considered, partly by external causal influences. Hence with respect to purely material events it is not correct to speak of an inner or fundamental indeterminism. Such an indeterminism could mean either that there is a total absence of determination, which is against the principle of causality, or that there is self-determination as in free will, which is impossible in a purely material nature. At most, therefore, one could speak of indeterminism with respect to our knowledge. However, the use of the term 'indeterminism' in this sense is contrary to established practice and can only lead to mis-understandings. Hence it should be avoided.[3]

IV. THE SPECIES—INDIVIDUAL STRUCTURE

Individual and Species. In the realm of experience one has always to do with individual things. Everything has its own existence; this thing is not that thing. Nevertheless, it is accepted, intuitively, as it were, without any further consideration, that there are groups of individuals which have a common nature; in other words, that there are individuals of the same species. For example, Socrates, Plato, and Aristotle are individual beings, yet each of them is a man; they are individuals of the species 'man'. Such a species-individual structure is found also in the vegetative and the animal kingdoms and even in inanimate nature. Hence with respect to the characteristics and activities of an individual a distinction has to be made between those belonging to the individual as an individual and others that belong to the individual insofar as it represents a species. A human being, for instance, has characteristics which are strictly individual and therefore differ from those of other individuals, but he has also properties which flow from his human nature and therefore are common to all individuals of the species 'man'. The same distinction has to be made in the vegetative and animal kingdoms, in which individual differences between members of the same species are often very striking. The same applies, with due changes, to inanimate matter. Here also the investigation has to begin with individual things; yet it is not primarily the individual which holds our interests, but the 'species' represented by the individual. In the ordinary usage of speech one does not even speak of individuals with respect to inanimate matter. For this reason it is all the more important to point out that in the scientific investigation of inanimate nature a species-individual structure must necessarily be presupposed if one desires to arrive at useful results. For science, and especially the science of nature, aims at results that have a general value for an entire species. Only exceptionally will science be interested in the nature and the behavior of the individual object as such; yet its investigations always have to start from individual things. Physics, for example, wants to arrive at knowledge of the physical properties of copper, water, and

---

[3]Concerning this matter, see P. Henry van Laer, *Philosophico-Scientific Problems* (*Duquesne Studies,* vol. 3), Pittsburgh, 1953, Ch. V.

helium or of magnetism and electricity; yet to obtain its results it has to start from the observation of individual samples of copper, water, and helium or that of individual magnets and solenoids and individually determined electric charges. Chemistry aims at imparting knowledge of species of matter, such as iron, sodium, or hydrochloric acid; yet in its endeavors to find such specific knowledge it has to start from the observation of individual samples of iron, sodium, or hydrochloric acid, and accepts without question that the samples of the same kind are equivalent with respect to their specific properties.

Science Presupposes the Species-Individual Structure. Within the limits of these sciences there are no means of proving the validity of such a presupposition. Every effort to prove its validity by means of scientific methods assumes what has to be proved. If, for instance, a scientist wants to prove that various samples of iron are really iron by comparing their properties with those listed in chemical tables, he is presupposing the species-individual structure, for these tables do not list data about this individual piece of matter, but at most data about other individual samples of the same kind. Thus we see that in order to justify its own existence, physical science must presuppose that in the realms of its subject matter there exists something like a species-individual structure of matter. Evidently, this is a presupposition which imposes itself upon the human mind without any difficulty, but cannot be justified by the specialized sciences themselves. It is the task of the philosophy of nature to make this presupposition intelligible by means of a consideration concerning the inner structure of matter.[4]

Accordingly, with respect to physical research, it will be necessary to be on guard lest individual characteristics be taken for specific properties. It can easily happen that, from previous uses or exposure to certain influences in nature or in the laboratory, a piece of matter or a sample of a liquid or gas has acquired characteristics which do not belong to the species as such. In order to prevent such mistakes, observation usually is not limited to one individual case but extended to many individual cases under a variety of conditions. To perform this investigation in the best possible way the methods mentioned above, in Section II, are used. If in the various individual cases a

---

[4]Regarding the problem of the species-individual structure, cf. Louis de Raeymaeker, *The Philosophy of Being,* St. Louis, 1954, pp. 155-169; and Andrew G. van Melsen, *The Philosophy of Nature (Duquesne Studies, Philosophical Series,* no. 2), 2nd ed., Pittsburgh, 1954, pp. 7 ff. and 115-125.

regular connection is found, one may conclude that the connection must belong to the 'species' as such by virtue of the proper 'specific' structure of its nature.

Remarks. 1. It may be noted that the term 'species' does not necessarily have to be taken here in the biological sense, but in general as the common element of which the individual instances are considered to be representative. A magnetic piece of iron, for example, may be taken to represent the species 'iron' or that of 'magnetic body', and, depending upon the nature of the investigation, even the genus 'metal' or that of 'solid body'. But the conclusions reached will always refer to an abstract whole which the individuals happen to represent.

2. According to the preceding discussions, the methods used in science presuppose that equal properties or activities find their foundation in the same specific nature. For it is on the basis of the identity of the properties revealed by this piece of matter with properties found elsewhere in other pieces of iron that one concludes : this piece of matter represents the species of 'iron'. Such a procedure assumes that in nature there is constancy of basic properties, and that at least in material nature everything takes place in a deterministic way. This point has been dealt with in our discussion of the principle of regularity.

Cultural Sciences. Insofar as cultural sciences consider groups of human beings, as is the case with economics, sociology, and ethnology, they also assume that the various human beings are specifically the same. Even cultural sciences, such as history, which occupy themselves with individual human beings cannot escape this presupposition, because the behavior of individuals cannot be understood and explained unless it be compared with that of other individuals in similar circumstances.

Thus it is clear that the species-individual structure is a general presupposition of all sciences of experience. It is a presupposition to which the human mind surrenders spontaneously, but which the specialized sciences themselves cannot justify. Philosophy, however, can take it as a starting point of more profound considerations.

V. PROBLEMS CONCERNING THE COMBINATION OF EXPERIENTIAL DATA

In order to arrive at a general statement about, e.g., certain phenomena of nature, it will usually be necessary to consider and combine experiential data that have been obtained at different times, in different places, and in different individual instances. For example, from the investigation of the behavior of different individual magnets made in different laboratories at different times conclusions are drawn with respect to magnets or magnetism in general, and in these conclusions abstraction is made from whatever was concrete and individual in the investigated material. Such a procedure is based upon the general presupposition that the behavior of nature is uniform, i.e., that the activities and qualities of material objects are constant. This constancy itself presupposes: 1) that the essence of material objects in nature is constant, and 2) that these activities are fully determined by the proper nature of the material objects, i.e. the *determinism* of nature, considered above, in Section III of this chapter. The general presupposition regarding the uniformity of nature implies, apart from this determinism and the species-individual structure, the following special presuppositions:

1. *Irrelevancy of time,* i.e. *per se* the time at which the observation is made and the duration of the observation do not exercise any influence upon the results of the observation.

2. *Irrelevancy of place,* i.e. *per se* the place at which the observation is made does not exercise any influence upon the results of the observation.

Both these special presuppositions will be considered briefly here.

1. *Irrelevancy of Time*

The way in which research is carried out in practice evidently presupposes that the element of time is *per se* irrelevant to the results of the observation. As a matter of fact, observations made at different times, whether it be a question of minutes or days, years or even centuries, are combined by the observers without the slightest hesitation, evidently because it appears to be manifest that time as such does not influence the observation. Of course, we do not mean that a careful investigator will not take note of the time of an observation. But he does not do it because he considers time itself relevant to the observation, but because the exact moment of time may have importance inasmuch as in the evaluation of the data of experience one must take into account factors which may have been present at a given moment of time or which in the passage of time may have undergone variations. Nevertheless the investigator is convinced that in itself time is extrinsic to the observed phenomena. The phenomena take place in time, but are not directly influenced by time. True, it is often said that time changes things, but this expression means merely that in the course of time a change will occur under the action of internal forces or external causes, and not that time itself exercises a causal influence.

On the other hand, occurrences which take place at different moments of time are considered to be individually different, even if they are entirely the same in other respects, as for example similar elements or phases in a periodic motion. Thus we are led to the conclusion that time is supposed to be a principle of individuation.

Accordingly, we may say that the procedure used in the method of experiential investigation presupposes 1) that of itself time has no influence upon the results of the observation; and 2) that time may be considered as a principle of individuation. It is not possible for us to enter into a detailed consideration to justify these presuppositions. We merely want to point out that they are presuppositions of the special sciences that use the method of scientific induction. For their justification we may refer the reader to *ex professo* treatises of the philosophy of nature which consider these questions.[5]

However, to prevent misunderstandings, we would like to remark that we do not consider time as something absolute having an independent existence. Time requires as its ontological foundation an existing reality which changes continuously (e.g. the motion of the earth round its axis and around the sun), and as its epistemological or psychological element an intellectual being which is capable of perceiving such a real change and numbering its successive phases.

2. *Irrelevancy of Place*

As a simple reflection shows, the way in which the investigator of nature proceeds in practice implies the presupposition that the place where a phenomenon occurs and the place at which the observer is located, in themselves, have no influence upon the result

---

[5]See, for example, P. Hoenen, *Cosmologia,* 4th ed., Rome 1949, pp. 237-260; *Philosophie der anorganische natuur,* Antwerpen-Nijmegen, 3rd ed., 1947, pp. 277-308; "De duratione successiva et de quaestionibus connexis", *Gregorianum,* vol. 34 (1953), pp. 3-31.

of the investigation. For, as a matter of fact, without any hesitation, one combines observations made at different places of the same laboratory or in different laboratories, even if they are situated at great distance from one another. Besides, use is made of observations performed at different times, i.e. when the earth occupied a different position with respect to the sun and the stars. Such a procedure can be justified only by the conviction that the place of an event or of its observer is, in itself, of no importance for the results of the observation. Obviously, the place of a phenomenon or its observer may have importance for the investigation in an accidental way, for the presence at a determinate place may mean that the phenomenon undergoes the influence of variable factors working at that place. For this reason it may be important to repeat at different places observation made in one body or in similar bodies in order to eliminate possible dependence of phenomena upon purely local conditions. Nevertheless there is a conviction that place as such is extrinsic to the observed phenomenon and therefore irrelevant to the occurrence of the phenomenon at a given place. The relationship of place is merely an extrinsic relationship which presupposes contact with other extended bodies and is determined by these other bodies.

In the foregoing we have spoken intentionally of *place* rather than of *space,* as might have been expected by some because time and space usually are mentioned together. In our opinion, the relation of place is the primary concept, and space a secondary concept deduced from it. Space, as such, is a figment of the imagination and has no reality of its own. Again, however, it would lead us too far afield to enter into details. We may refer the reader to studies concerning the philosophy of nature in which the question of place and space is considered.[6]

VI. THE FOUNDATION OF THE SPECIAL METHODS OF INVESTIGATION

Preliminary Remarks. As has been mentioned, to discover a certain necessary connection and isolate it from other, contingent, phenomena may entail prolonged and varied investigations. The reason is that there are always very many factors at work in nature,

---

[6]See, e.g. P. Hoenen, *Cosmologia*, pp. 64-109; *Philosophie der anorganische natuur*, pp. 125-194; P. H. van Laer, *Actio in Distans en aether, Utrecht*, 1947, pp. 15-48.

and *a priori* it is not at all clear which factors are pertinent. Sometimes, for instance, it will be temperature which is important; at other times, temperature is irrelevant, but weight, inner or outer structure, local conditions, etc. are relevant. Nature usually offers an entangled mass of phenomena, and it is up to the man of research to disentangle the complexity of facts by eliminating the irrelevant and retaining the relevant. To accomplish this task in the best possible way, various special methods have been devised, especially for the physical sciences. These methods are often called 'Mill's Canons', because John Stuart Mill was the first to describe them in detail. However, the detailed study of these methods belongs to the philosophy of physical science; hence we will restrict ourselves to a general consideration of their foundation.

Before we can do so, it will be necessary first to point out the distinction between two kinds of scientific induction. This induction will always lead to a universal statement, but the nature of this statement may be either causal or non-causal. Thus we must distinguish between non-causal or *'acausal'* and *causal* induction.

1. *Acausal Induction*

The universal statement resulting from induction will sometimes express a necessary connection without saying anything about the causes involved. In such a case the statement is said to be *'non-causal'* or *'acausal'*. It merely gives a *description* of a definite group of phenomena according to their necessary or essential relationships. It will describe, for instance, that a certain property or activity belongs of necessity to a specifically determined subject, or that two specifically determined phenomena A and B necessarily occur together. Because in such cases the statement resulting from the inductive process does not say anything about the pertinent causal factors, the process itself may be called *non-causal* or rather *acausal induction*. The question regarding the causes remains provisionally undecided and will have to be solved by means of a further investigation which may be termed *causal induction*. Instead of 'non-causal' it will be preferable to use 'acausal', because there is less likelihood that this term will be misunderstood.

2. *Causal Induction*

The causal induction aims at a general statement concerning the foundation of properties or activities, the causes of a phenomenon, or

the basis of the necessary connection between two specifically determined phenomena. It intends to give an *explanation* by means of
causes. In this connection the term 'causes' should be understood
in a wider sense, i.e. it refers not only to efficient causes, but applies
also to material, formal, and final causes. As a rule, the causal investigation is much more complex than an acausal one, especially if the
purpose is not merely to discover the 'global' or common cause of
certain phenomena, but precisely that cause which by its very nature
directly produces this effect or phenomenon and no other, the so-called
cause *primo et per se*.

3. *The Principles upon Which the Methods are Based*

As we have seen above, both causal and acausal scientific induction
try to arrive at general statements concerning a necessary or essential connection, whatever be the nature of this connection, whether
that of subject and property, that of conjoined phenomena, or that of
cause and effect. The starting point lies here in the experiential
research which in the observation of concrete and individual phenomena looks for regularity. Because regularity in material nature
always implies necessity, as we have seen in Section III, it will be
best to start from the implications of the concept 'necessary' to discover the principles which justify these general scientific methods.
In this way it will be easy to find the foundation of these methods if
we start with the statement that "necessary or essential is whatever
under given conditions cannot not-be or be different from what it
actually is". This fundamental statement implies the following three
principles :

1. The necessary must be positively present in all relevant
instances.

2. The necessary cannot be absent in any relevant instance.

3. If one phenomenon changes, the phenomenon that is necessarily connected with it will have to change accordingly.

Let us formulate these principles more completely.

1. Whenever a phenomenon (or property, or effect, or cause)
occurs or is present, all elements which are necessarily connected
with it or presupposed by it (other phenomenon, or subject, or proper
cause, or effect) must also occur or be present.

2. Whenever a phenomenon (or subject, or cause, or effect) is absent, all elements which are of necessity connected with it (other phenomenon, or property, or proper effect) or by their very nature capable of producing it (proper cause) must also be absent.

3. Whenever a phenomenon (or subject, or cause, or effect) varies, all elements which are of necessity connected with it (other phenomenon, or property, or proper effect, or proper cause) must show corresponding variations.

With respect to the second and third of these principles, due caution must be observed in drawing any conclusion. For it is possible for one and the same phenomenon P, e.g. a change in temperature, to be brought about by the activity of different causal factors, A, B, C, etc. In such a case the absence of A does not allow the conclusion that P also will be absent, for P can be present because of the action of B or C. However, if P is strictly the proper effect of A, the absence of P will imply the absence of A, and vice versa. For this reason the formulas use the term 'proper cause' and 'proper effect', to indicate that the principles are concerned with connections which can have only one explanation.

Remark. Evidently, these principles themselves presuppose 1) the general validity of the principle of causality or, more broadly, the principle of sufficient reason; and 2) the determinism of nature, i.e. that in material nature everything takes place deterministically. For if any uncaused phenomenon could occur, or if non-deterministic (free) causes could play a role, these principles would lose their general validity, and the very foundation of the methods of investigation in question would crumble.

4. *Special Norms of Scientific Investigation*

From the preceding considerations it is possible to derive several theses that can serve as special norms in the investigation of phenomena.

1. *In Acausal Induction.* The special norms are as follows:

a. If the presence of phenomenon A is constantly and invariably accompanied by phenomenon B, then there is a necessary connection between these two phenomena.

b. If the absence of this phenomenon A is always and invariably accompanied by the absence of phenomenon B (or if in the absence of phenomenon A, which is probably connected with phenomenon B, phenomenon B also is absent), then this indicates a necessary connection between these phenomena.

c. If a variation in phenomenon A is always accompanied by a variation in phenomenon B, then there is a necessary connection between these two phenomena.

These theses guide the acausal investigation insofar as observation and experimentation will be directed to discover whether or not:

a. Phenomenon B always accompanies or follows phenomenon A (proof);

b. Phenomenon B does not occur in the absence of this phenomenon A (counterproof);

c. Phenomenon B varies when phenomenon A varies (variation proof).

It will not always be possible to perform observation or experimentation in accordance with all three of these norms. Sometimes, for instance, only the third norm can be followed in observations. But even in such a case there will still be a possibility of arriving at certain statements regarding a definite necessary relationship. However, it is beyond our scope to enter into details in this matter.

2. In Causal Induction. Of course, in this type of induction attention has to be paid only to the relationship cause-effect. So we get the following norms:

a. If the cause is present, its proper effect will of necessity be present.

b. If the cause is absent, its proper effect will of necessity be absent.

c. If the cause is varied, the proper effect will vary accordingly.

These theses guide the causal investigation insofar as observation and experimentation can be reduced to these three points:

a. Does phenomenon Q occur in the presence of phenomenon P? (Proof).

b. Does phenomenon Q not occur in the absence of this phenomenon P? (Counterproof).

c. Does phenomenon Q vary if phenomenon P is varied? (Variation Proof).

Here also it will not always be possible to observe all of these three norms. In addition, it should be evident that such an investigation will have to be carried out with all the necessary prudence.

Remark. The above-mentioned norms of scientific investigation are, of course, also especially important for the verification of scientific hypotheses and theories, as we will see in the next chapter.

VII. CHARACTER AND VALUE OF THE GENERAL CONCLUSIONS OBTAINED BY SCIENTIFIC INDUCTION

Value. From the preceding discussions it follows that the conclusion of an incomplete or scientific induction has a value which far exceeds its origin in the confines of the special science concerned. For this origin consisted of the observation of individual instances in concrete conditions, whereas the resulting conclusion claims to be of a universal validity. This claim, as we have seen, is entirely justified because the conclusion is not based merely upon the data of experience, but also upon universally valid principles which are implicitly accepted in scientific induction, such as the principles of regularity, of sufficient reason and of causality, and also upon insights into the nature of matter, such as the determinism of nature, the irrelevancy (*per se*) of place and time, and the species-individual structure of matter. In the special sciences these principles and insights may be presupposed and intuitively, as it were, accepted, but in philosophy they can be given their justification. Hence we may conclude that the practice of scientific investigators, especially in the physical sciences, is entirely correct and justified, provided the general principles upon which this practice is based are accepted.

Character. Presupposing that the inductive process has been executed correctly, one may say that the resulting statements have a character of necessity. Nevertheless, this necessity is quite different from the necessity which is proper to metaphysical principles and statements, or that of mathematical theses, which are based upon an insight into the essence of things. While it is true that the necessity of inductive statements is founded ontologically upon the essence of things, it remains true that we do not have any direct knowledge of these specific essences. For this reason our knowledge can be deficient in many respects, and these deficiencies will reveal themselves in the inductive conclusions. Hence is is important to keep in mind that the necessity of a statement established by induction is merely *relative* or *hypothetical*. By these terms we mean that the statement in which this necessity is expressed is valid only:

1) In the universe as it actually is, and not in any possible material universe;

2) For that part of the particular domain which has been investigated by means of observation and experimentation;

3) With the degree of exactness which is warranted by this observation and experimentation.

Hence, theoretically at least, a statement established by induction remains always open to revision, extension, restriction, and more accurate formulation (cf. Ch. IV, Sect. II, 2).

VIII. VARIOUS PHILOSOPHICAL VIEWS OF SCIENTIFIC INDUCTION

Although this chapter is becoming disproportionately long in comparison with the others, the primordial importance of the question makes it mandatory to add a few remarks concerning the various philosophical views of scientific induction and its past history.

It is obvious that the epistemological value of scientific induction will be appreciated differently in accordance with the view one holds with respect to the existence and nature of an extramental world and the nature of our knowledge of the same. Of the many philosophical views concerning these matters, we shall briefly mention a few.

The Realistic View. This is the viewpoint that has been tacitly assumed in the preceding pages, because, in our opinion, the realistic view is the only one which can be maintained. Realism admits the existence of an extramental world and the capacity of our cognitive faculties to know this reality, and especially the capacity of the intellect to arrive at general insights into reality. In the first place, the general principles, such as the principles of sufficient reason, causality, and the determinism of nature, which form the basis of scientific induction, are not merely established habits of thinking, but valid for an outer world which is independent of our thinking. Secondly, this view is not naively accepted as evident by a kind of natural instinct, as extreme realists seem to think, but can be established by convincing rational arguments. However, the justification of this epistemological position falls beyond the scope of this study, and we must refer the reader to *ex professo* treatises of realistic epistemology.[7]

The Empiristic View. According to empiricism, intellectual knowledge is not essentially different from sensitive knowledge; hence scientific knowledge cannot transcend the data of sense experience. Consequently, an abstractly general or universal knowledge of the world of experience is impossible. Accordingly, the result of so-called scientific induction cannot be more than an aggregate of particular sense experiences. In this way, an inductive statement is merely collectively general, and therefore there is no essential difference between scientific induction and complete or by-analogy-completed induction (Cf. Ch. VII, Sect. I).

Moreover, according to many empiricists, the result obtained by scientific induction has no value for reality because it expresses merely something about a subjective association of our mind. Although a so-called general judgment may be certain with respect to the particular data of sense experience, which formed its starting point, it does not give any certainty with respect to future experience. At most, it can offer a basis for probable expectations.

Empiricism is allied to modern pragmatism, which attaches value to the results of induction only insofar as they can offer useful norms for our intellectual, moral and social life. Inductive statements are considered to have no objective value with respect to reality, but may be able to help us to make use of fleeting reality.

The Conceptualistic and Kantian View. According to Kant and his followers, the principles upon which scientific induction is based are synthetic *a priori* judgments. Hence they have compelling value only with respect to the so-called phenomenal world. Because of the very nature of our intellect, we are forced to admit that the phenomena of our world occur and are determined in accordance with the strict laws of causality. Lachelier added the category of finality to those established by Kant and said that this category gives us the inner conviction that the phenomena of this world occur with regularity because all activity is directed towards a purpose.

---

[7]See, for instance, F. Van Steenberghen, *Epistemology*, New York, 1949.

Thus, according to the proponents of this philosophical view, the scientific systems of experiential sciences rest upon a mere blind synthesis of phenomena which the intellect has to make in accordance with certain innate laws of thinking. There can be no question of objective representation of real events occurring in a real world.

The Occasionalistic View. According to occasionalism, whose best-known exponent is Malebranche (1638-1715), there is no true causality in created things. Creatures are mere occasions for the exercise of divine activity. Apparently, effects are produced by creatures, but in reality they can be due only to God, who is the first and only cause of all that is. Obviously, in this view there can be no question of a necessary connection based upon the essence of things. Scientific induction does not teach us anything about an activity which finds its origin in the nature of things; at most, it can say something about the activity of God with respect to created things. Leibniz (1646-1716), also, may be considered to belong to this group because he denies creatures any activity of their own. As a philosophical system occasionalism is quite dead and retains merely an historical importance.

If the realistic view alone, as we think, is true, the other views, of course, are bound to be false. Besides, serious arguments can be presented against each of the other views in particular. Again, however, it is beyond the purpose of this study to discuss these matters.

IX. SOME REMARKS CONCERNING THE HISTORY OF SCIENTIFIC INDUCTION

It is often claimed that Francis Bacon (1561-1626) discovered the inductive method and proposed its first schematic form. John Stuart Mill (1806-1873) is supposed to have formulated the first more complete theory of induction. Specifically, the method of induction would have been unknown in scholastic philosophy. These claims, however, are not correct.

Even before Aristotle, induction was used as a matter of fact by Socrates, who by means of series of questions and answers concerning concrete objects and relationships endeavored to arrive at general concepts and principles. Aristotle (384-322 B.C.) himself, knew induction, at least in its fundamental characteristics, and thus in this problem, too, Aristotelian-Thomistic philosophy was able to place itself upon an Aristotelian foundation. Both deduction (apagôgè) and induction (epagôgè) were known to Aristotle who compared and contrasted them. He speaks about induction in the sense of what we have called complete induction, e.g., in *Prior Analytics,* Bk. II, Ch. 23 (68b 28). He knew also that a complete enumeration is not always necessary, and that it may be sufficient to apprehend the phenomena in another suitable manner. To quote a few texts, in his *Prior Analytics,* he says:

> It is the business of experience to give the principles which belong to each subject. I mean for example that astronomical experience supplies the principles of astronomical science: for once the phenomena were adequately apprehended, the demonstrations of astronomy were discovered.[8]

And in his *Posterior Analytics* he writes about induction:

> Out of sense-perception comes to be what we have called memory, and out of frequently repeated memories of the same thing develops experience; for a number of memories constitute an experience. From experience, again—i.e. from the universal now established in its entirety within the soul, the one beside the many which is a single identity within them all—originate the skill of the craftsman and the knowledge of the man of science, skill in the sphere of coming to be and science in the sphere of being.[9]

Similar statements were made by the medieval scholastics. It remains true, however, that induction, as it is used in the physical sciences, was better understood and more accurately formulated in later times when there was a greater abundance of means to perform scientific investigations. Francis Bacon and especially John Stuart Mill did excellent work in this field. Nevertheless, the remark must be made that their theoretical foundation was empiristic, so that, in their opinion, this induction could have no more value than complete induction or induction completed by analogy. However, as we have seen above, the method indicated by them allows conclusions which go beyond these two types of induction.

---

[8]Bk. I, Ch. 30; 46a 28ff.
[9]Bk. II, Ch. 19; 100a 4ff.

CHAPTER NINE

HYPOTHESIS AND THEORY

INTRODUCTION

In the construction and development of a science a very important function must be assigned to the so-called scientific theory. Its role in the sciences is so important and far-reaching that it is impossible to treat it within the limited scope of this work with anything even remotely resembling adequacy. We will therefore have to limit ourselves to some aspects of the subject which are important for the scope of this study. On the other hand, we will not only consider the theory with respect to physical science, as is often done, but extend our considerations to the ideal sciences and the group of experiential sciences which are usually indicated by the terms 'sciences of man' and 'cultural sciences' (*Geisteswissenschaften*).[1] Usually, however, the examples will be borrowed from physical science because in this science the characteristic elements are most strikingly present.

As will become clear in subsequent pages, the meaning of the term 'theory' is not always exactly the same. Generally speaking, however, the term is used to indicate a connected system of theses, all of which have been logically deduced from certain basic theses. In accordance with the nature of the basic theses and the intentions of their author, theories acquire a different character; hence in the various groups of sciences theories will show a variety of characters. Especially, there is a great difference between the theories of ideal sciences and those of experiential sciences.[2]

Division of This Chapter. Because of the above-mentioned difference in character of theories, it appears advisable to devote the first section of this chapter to the theory in ideal sciences, and the second to the theory in experiential sciences. The third section will be dedicated to the formulation of hypotheses and theories, while the

---

[1]This division of the sciences and the proper character of the various groups will be considered in the second volume of this work. For the correct understanding of what follows here a superficial knowledge of the various groups is sufficient.

[2]Because this study is primarily concerned with the sciences in the sense of special sciences, we will not speak about philosophic theories, although many of our considerations will apply also to these theories.

fourth will consider the verification of scientific theories. In the last section we will speak about the truth value of theories in the experiential sciences.

I. THE THEORY IN THE IDEAL SCIENCES

As will be explained in the second volume, the group of ideal sciences embraces all those sciences whose specific contents is not taken from experience but produced by the human mind, although it must be admitted, of course, that ultimately some of their basic concepts and theses have been derived from experience, albeit a very primordial experience. Once these basic concepts have been acquired, the human mind is capable of using them in a fairly arbitrary way, as long as care is taken not to go against the essential contents of these concepts and to avoid contradiction in the basic theses or relationships of the concepts which the mind wants to accept as the foundation of its scientific construction. These basic theses are usually called *axioms* or *postulates*.

The Ideal Theory as Exemplified in Mathematics. Among others, the mathematical sciences and logical calculi belong to the ideal sciences. We shall limit our examples to mathematics and specifically to that which is important for our immediate point of view, because the proper character of the ideal sciences in general and the mathematical sciences in particular shall be considered more extensively in the second volume of this work.

In pure mathematics, the starting point is a set of axioms or postulates which determine the basic properties of the elements used in the construction of a mathematical system. As an example we may point to Euclidean geometry, with which everyone is sufficiently acquainted to recognize in it the essential features of ideal science. In Euclidean geometry postulates determine what is to be understood by a point, straight line, surface, etc., and the basic properties one wants to attribute to them. In addition, it is assumed that certain basic operations can be performed; for instance, that it is possible to draw a straight line through two points or that it is possible to describe a circle with a given point as its center and a given length of line as its radius. In this way a foundation is laid upon which the whole structure of Euclidean geometry can be built by logical deduction.[3]

---

[3]We abstract from certain fundamental insights which are indispensable in the construction of mathematics, although they are not usually accounted for

Theorems which have been deduced from these basic concepts and axioms in a logically correct way are unerringly true with an inner necessity that is perfectly clear to us. However, this necessity is hypothetical because 'it is dependent upon the starting point. If the Euclidean postulates are taken as the starting point, the theorems, as they are deduced in Euclidean geometry, are of necessity true; hence their necessity is hypothetical.

It is possible to replace one or more postulates by others provided care is taken not to introduce any internal contradictions into the new set of postulates. If, for example, the Euclidean postulate of parallel lines is replaced by another, such as the postulate that through a point outside a straight line no straight line can be drawn parallel to the first, the result is another, non-Euclidean, geometry. This non-Euclidean geometry has the same inner consistency and is equally free from contradictions as Euclidean geometry, but its logical deductions lead to theorems which, although in this system they are true of necessity, deviate from the Euclidean theorems. Accordingly, such theorems in themselves have no absolute necessity, but only a hypothetical necessity which is dependent upon the freely chosen starting point. A similar hypothetical character is found in many parts of mathematics as well as in logical calculi (Cf. Ch. IV, Sect. II, 1).

Such parts of mathematics or logical calculus may be considered as one great theory in which the axioms or postulates constitute the starting point. Instead of Euclidean geometry one could speak also of the Euclidean theory of mathematical space. In a similar way, there is question of the number theory, group theory, etc. Accordingly, in ideal sciences theories have a very special character of their own. They are not a means used by science in its development, as is the case with theories in the experiential sciences, but they themselves constitute the science.

Ideal Theory and Reality. Because pure mathematics does not borrow its postulates from experience if a few basic concepts and fundamental insights are excepted, pure mathematics is not concerned with the question whether or not its deduced theorems have value for experience. Often, however, this does not prevent the acquired insights of pure mathematics from being applicable to experience. For example, if the data of experience allow the postulates of Euclidean

---

in the form of postulates: for instance, that the extended is divisible; the whole greater than its part; and quantities may be added to other quantities of the same kind.

geometry to be considered as a meaningful idealization of reality, then the deduced theorems will be applicable to this reality. The same may be said with respect to non-Euclidean geometry, number theory or other parts of mathematics. A logical calculus, likewise, will find a possibility of application if a meaningful content can be given to its basic postulates.

Ideal Theory and Verification. From the preceding considerations it should be clear that there can be no question of a genuine verification of such theories by means of experience. The only possible verification consists in the controlled correctness of the logical deduction of the theorems. An experiment might show, as was proposed by Gauss, that in a triangle whose sides are formed by light rays the sum of the angles is really equal to two right angles, as it has to be in Euclidean geometry. Nevertheless, this experiment would not verify that Euclidean geometry is the only true geometry, but would determine only that the artificial triangle and the structure of these real surroundings are capable of being suitably described by Euclidean geometry. As a matter of fact, Euclidean geometry in general appears to be excellently suited for the description of the mathematical aspects of terrestrial phenomena. This suitability is rather obvious because the postulates upon which Euclidean geometry is based, specifically the postulate of parallel lines, is suggested by experience. Nevertheless, as a mathematical theory, non-Euclidean geometry has perfectly the same value as the Euclidean system. Moreover, the possibility must not be excluded that with respect to certain metric applications in our world a non-Euclidean geometry would be just as good if not more useful than the Euclidean system.

These remarks should be sufficient to give some insight into the proper character of hypotheses and theories in the ideal sciences. We will come back to this point in the second volume.

II. THE THEORY IN THE EXPERIENTIAL SCIENCES

In experiential sciences frequent use is made of theories as means to aid in the development and building up of these sciences. The value, however, of the theory as such a means is not always the same. Although it is true that the formulation of a theory is always guided by the intention of acquiring more insight into the subject matter under consideration, nevertheless the ways in which this insight is brought about may be totally different in different theories, and consequently the character of the theories themselves may vary considerably. In order to obtain a good insight into the nature and structure of theories in the experiential sciences, we will endeavor to divide them in a responsible way into groups, although we fully realize how full of pitfalls such an enterprise is.

Every effort to arrive at a motivated division must pay careful attention to the purpose for which the theory is devised and consequently also to the way in which the foundations or hypotheses of the theory are arrived at. In our opinion, the first distinction to be made is that between temporary and permanent theories. By *temporary theories* are meant theories which serve exclusively as means in scientific research to arrive at definite results and therefore have only a temporary character. *Permanent theories,* on the other hand, are theories which serve as means to acquire an insight into the definite results of experience and therefore have, at least if they are verified, a more permanent nature, so that they are able to retain a place in the edifice of science. It is especially the second group which is meant when there is question of scientific theories. Both groups shall be considered here successively.

1. *Theories of a Temporary Nature*

Description of this Type of Theory. When in the preceding chapter we considered scientific induction, there was question also of the investigation which has to precede the inductive conclusion, and specific mention was made of the special methods of investigation which in physical science are often indicated by the term "Mill's Canons". Before these methods can be applied successfully, usually a substantial amount of preliminary research will have to be made. The research begins with the gathering of the various data of experience—data of the present and the past; data acquired by unaided sense observation or with the help of instruments; data obtained with the maximum possible variation of conditions. A second phase, which accompanies or follows the first, consists in the critical study and sifting of the experiential data in order to obtain a better view of their possible connections and relationships. In simple cases this connection may be discovered in this second phase itself. If the case is more difficult, however, this discovery usually will not yet be made, but perhaps there will be already a conjecture, idea or conception of the probable connection and then this conjecture may serve as a directing principle in further research. This conjecture or conception, also called *hypothesis,* may simply refer to a connection without indicating a cause, as is the case in acausal (non-causal) research (cf. Ch. VIII, Sect. VI), or it may be concerned precisely with the probable cause of a phenomenon or complex of phenomena. In both cases such a hypothesis is able to direct further research and render possible the rational use of the above-mentioned methods of investigation. In difficult cases, where a given hypothesis is not immediately verifiable or the situation is not clear, an effort has to be made to arrive at verifiable consequences in a logico-deductive way with the aid of established data. This may be done by means of proof, counter-proof, and variation proof. The whole of deduced theses together with the appropriate argumentation may be called a *theory.* Such theories again are either acausal or causal.

Examples. It is easy to indicate examples of these theories in the various realms of the sciences. For instance, the theory which guided Pasteur in his investigation of the origin of living bodies; the various hypotheses and theories concerning the origin of some disease, e.g. beri-beri; the theories regarding the connection between sunspots and other phenomena in the sun and in the atmosphere of the earth; theories about the origin of Novae, etc.

Hypotheses and theories may be successfully used also in the investigation of the nature of *individual* things or concrete relationships. For instance, there are hypotheses and theories concerning the origin of the Alps, the inner structure of the Earth, the origin of the Moon and the Crab Nebula. If subsequent research would confirm any one of these hypotheses, it would have lost its original value for science, which is that of a pure aid to research.

In cultural sciences, too, similar hypotheses and theories are often used in the work of research. However, because of special difficulties proper to these sciences, success is not so easily obtained, at least not in the sense that unequivocal verification is reached. A few easy examples of such hypotheses and their corresponding theories are, for instance, in history, those concerning the time of origin and the authorship of the Odyssey and the Iliad; those regarding the descent of Columbus and his purpose in sailing westward; in philology, those with respect to the author of the well-known book THE IMITATION OF CHRIST. As a recent example in classical philology one could name the decipherment by Michael Ventris of the so-called 'Minoan Linear B Script', which was first discovered in Knossos

(Crete). Starting from the hypothesis that he had to do with an early stage of Greek and taking the supposed relationship of this language to Greek as his basis, Ventris was able to work out a theory concerning word forms and endings which would have to occur in the discovered texts. His careful investigation led to a perfect verification of his hypothesis, so that this theory has no longer any other than purely historical value.

Character of the Temporary Theory. The typical characteristic of these hypotheses and theories is that in the intention of their user they have a purely temporary character and serve only as an aid and directing principle in scientific research. Once this research has brought more light in the matter, i.e. has shown that the hypothesis in question is either not tenable or verified by the facts, then the theory has accomplished its task and disappears from the scene. At most, it will retain a place in a book concerned with the history of science.

Notwithstanding the fact that by their very purpose these theories have a purely provisional nature, it is quite possible that they will continue to exist for centuries because a definite 'conclusion has not yet been possible. On the other hand, it may happen also that a theory which has played a role in scientific research and has been verified, will subsequently, with or without being perfected and refined, acquire a place among the permanent theories to be considered in the next part of this chapter. This will be the case if the theory in question is sufficiently important and comprehensive to describe or explain a large group of phenomena. Thus it may happen that of two competing temporary theories one will be abandoned while the other, which has been proved to be correct, will be given a permanent place in science. The corpuscular theory of light, for instance, as formulated by Newton, has disappeared from the scene at least in its original form, but the competing wave theory of Huygens has remained, at least in its essential elements. In the next part of this chapter we shall come back to this point.

2. *Theories of a Permanent Nature*

By permanent theories we mean those theories which, at least in the intention of their inventors, have to play a permanent role in science as a system. Their purpose is to give an orderly arrangement to many isolated and varied data of experience and to make it possible to know the mutual connection or dependence of these data and to understand them.   There are two ways in which this purpose can be reached.

a. It is possible that only results which have been definitely established by scientific research are used in the foundation of a theory and no recourse is made to hypotheses concerning the mechanism or causes of the phenomena.   Such theories may be called *phenomenological, descriptive* or *classification* theories.

b. The second kind of theory wants to give a causal explanation of connected phenomena.   It aims at knowledge of the reason or foundation of the interconnection and dependence of phenomena.   For this reason theories of this kind are called *explanatory* theories.

Both types of theory shall be considered briefly in the following pages.[4]

a. PHENOMENOLOGICAL OR DESCRIPTIVE THEORIES

Description. The proper character of this group of theories, which makes them differ from explanatory theories, is best indicated in the following negative-positive way.   Phenomenological theories do not start from suppositions concerning the mechanism of phenomena or their causes; consequently they are not based upon a hypothesis in the usual sense of the term.   On the contrary, they are based upon general laws and principles which either are definitely established by scientific research or borrowed from the ideal sciences, especially mathematics.

The purpose of these theories, however, is not merely to describe isolated relationships or to enumerate special laws, but to acquire insight by means of a well-founded and reasoned description of phenomenal relationships in their mutual connection and dependence; by the integration of the particular into the more general, or by the deduction of special laws and relations from more general laws and relationships.   In this way there arises a natural whole, a grouping or classification of phenomena according to their factual connection. Thus an easy view of the whole is obtained, which is very suitable also for the acquisition of insight.   Insofar as these theories are based only upon that which is directly known from the observed phenomena—this knowledge, of course, is generalized by means of scientific induction— they may be called *phenomenological* or *descriptive* theories; and inso-

---

[4]Concerning the division of theories and the value for reality of both groups, cf. E. Huffer, "Over de realiteitswaarde en de structuur van de physische theorie", *Studiën*, jrg. 67 (1935), vol. 123, pp. 115-138.

far as they result in a rational classification of the observed phenomena, they are called *classification* theories.

As has been mentioned above, the foundation of these theories does not contain any hypothetical elements in the usual sense of the term. If occasionally in connection with these theories the term 'hypothesis' is used, it is taken in its original meaning as 'substructure', i.e. something which functions as the basis of the theoretical edifice,[5] or to indicate that the experiential result itself upon which the theory is based is still somewhat hypothetical in nature (cf. Ch. IV, Sect. II, and Ch. VIII, Sect. VII).

Examples. The classical example of such a phenomenological theory in physics is the theory of thermodynamics. This theory starts from two laws whose validity has been established by extensive experience. They are the law of conservation of energy and the law of entropy. From these general laws or 'principles' one can, first of all, deduce certain other general laws or principles which in a sense are equivalent to the law of entropy; e.g. the principle that free energy tends to a minimum. These general principles, in their turn, are applicable to numerous sectors of physical science, in such a way that known phenomena can be fitted into the general frame and others, as yet unknown, can be calculated and predicted. Thus an enormous mass of experiential data which otherwise would stand disconnectedly alongside one another are described and classified as a single great complex.

Accordingly, in the theory of thermodynamics, apart from the validity of the laws of thermodynamics and certain other definitely established data, no other hypotheses are introduced concerning the inner structure of things, the forces working in them, or any other matter. Given the main laws of thermodynamics, the course of all pertinent phenomena becomes clear. In a nature which is subject to these laws, the general course of phenomena, although proper to the respective spheres of the objects and subject to the special laws of these spheres, is dominated by these general laws.

Alongside such a phenomenological way of considering the experiential data, it is often possible to explain the same phenomena in a causal way with the aid of appropriate hypotheses and consequently in theories of a different, explanatory, nature. For example, many

---

[5]The Greek term *hypothesis* means the placing of the foundation of a problem: *hypo,* under, and *tithenai,* to place; hence literally, to place (a thing) under (something else).

of the phenomena which belong to thermodynamics allow also a causal explanation by means of the molecular theory. Another example of a phenomenological theory is Maxwell's theory of electricity, alongside which the electronic theory of Lorentz plays the role of an explanatory theory attempting to give a causal explanation.

For the foundation of a phenomenological theory use may be made of all laws and general rules established in experiential science by means of scientific induction. As far as the physical sciences are concerned, consideration in this respect is deserved, first of all, by the most general laws, which usually are also called 'principles'; e.g. the laws of conservation of energy, the law of entropy, the principle of inertia, the maximum and minimum principles of physics and mechanics. Other laws, however, also may be used if, although less general, they are nevertheless fundamental for a large field of experience; e.g. Coulomb's law or the law of equipotentiality in electricity, the laws of valence in chemistry, etc. Even more particular laws may be useful as building blocks of a phenomenological theory.

In the cultural sciences also there are similar general laws which can serve as the foundation of a phenomenological or descriptive theory; e.g. general economic laws or the sound laws of linguistics. As examples of economic theories one could name the theories of free trade, protective tariffs, wage determinants, devaluation and inflation. For these theories have as their foundation certain laws or tendencies, known from experience, which are capable of being used in mutual connections and from which certain conclusions can be deduced.

However, in the sciences of man as man, such as psychology, and in the cultural sciences, which study phenomena whose origin and contents are derived from the activity of man as a rational and free being, it will always be necessary to be on guard against the occurrence of deviations from the rules. As a free being, man is capable of expressing himself and acting in a way which in individual cases deflects from the general rule. Consequently, it may easily happen that there will be deviations with respect to the deduced consequences of the theory. In the second volume, when studying the experiential sciences, we will have to return to this point.

Phenomenological Theories Have an Acausal Character. All the laws or rules of phenomenological theories are of a typically acausal or non-causal nature, i.e. they are formulated in such a way that nothing is said about the mechanism or the producing causes of the phenomena, and the inventor of the theory also deliberately abstains from considering causality. The laws are intended only to express how, as a matter of fact, objects or men behave. As such, they are purely descriptive, and therefore the theories based upon them share to some extent in the same character. Nevertheless, as has been mentioned above, they are not purely descriptive, for they give us also a certain insight into the connection and interdependence of the phenomena and consequently an insight into the structure of natural objects, the universe or a realm of human activity. For this reason they are sometimes said to 'explain' things. But in the usual sense of the term, 'to explain' means to reduce to known causes. Hence if this term is used in connection with phenomenological theories, the only possible rational meaning is to make the particular intelligible through the general or, in appropriate cases, to deduce the less known and the unknown from the known or to reduce them to it. Even here one could speak of a causal explanation, provided the term 'cause' is not limited to efficient or producing causes, but allowed to extend to formal, material, and final causes. For example, in a theory which is based upon general laws of nature, such as the laws of energy and entropy, the formulas used say something about the actual structure of the world and therefore about 'formed matter' (material and formal cause), its actual order and inner finality (final cause). Nevertheless, in accordance with the customary usage of speech, we prefer to restrict the term 'cause' here to efficient causes and the term 'explanatory theory' to those theories which are really based upon known or supposedly known efficient causes. These explanatory theories must be considered now in the following part of this chapter.

b. Explanatory Theories

Description. The theories of this group have another purpose than the preceding type of theory. Explanatory theories, too, start from the data of experience, want to bring order in them and lead to insight, but the way in which they attempt to do it is different because they try to give understanding of the *why* and *how* of phenomena and to explain them through their *producing causes*. If these causes are not known but only their effect, it will be the task of research to formulate a *hypothesis* concerning the probable cause, whether of an individual and concrete phenomenon or, as usually is the case, of the specific nature of phenomena. Contrary to what happens in phenomenological theories, such an *explanatory* hypothesis is not a statement concerning what actually has been found to exist in nature, but a supposition concerning reality from which the actually observed facts have to follow by way of consequence. It is possible that such a hypothesis will make the observed fact or connection immediately intelligible. Often, however, the hypothesis will be used as a foundation upon which, with the help of other definitely established data and mathematical aids, a theory will be built in which deductively one arrives at consequences whose empirical verification is possible, either immediately or at least later. In case the theory arrives by deduction at consequences whose occurrence is still entirely unknown, the statements regarding these consequences will have the character of 'predictions', and further research will have to determine whether or not such a prediction is realized.

As long as a theory has not yet been wholly verified, and this means at least as long as competing theories exist which proclaim their ability to explain a group of phenomena, such a theory has a *provisional* nature. It may therefore be classified among the provisional causal theories. If, however, a fortunate choice has been made in the invention and formulation of a hypothesis, the theoretical consequences deduced from it will be observed to exist in reality. Reversely, as we shall see more in detail in the fourth section of this chapter, the hypothesis and theory will have to prove their value in a confrontation of the deduced consequences with reality. If a theory comes up to expectations and is verified by the facts, the phenomena concerned will have found their *explanation* in the sense that it is now understood why they have to occur and why precisely in this way. An explanatory theory which is concerned with a sufficiently important and broad sector of a science and has been wholly verified will retain a *permanent* place in this science, for even in the future such a theory will be indispensable for a good insight into the matter concerned.

Examples. As an illustration of the preceding considerations we may refer to the theory of light. To explain the phenomena of light known in the seventeenth century, Newton invented the corpuscular hypothesis and Huygens the wave hypothesis, which developed into the corpuscular and the wave theories of light. The consequences of both theories differed in many respects, but in the beginning experience did not offer a basis for making a choice between the two theories. Later, however, more refined experience showed that only the wave theory could give the desired explanation. While before the verification of the wave theory both theories had a provisional character, after it the wave theory acquired a permanent place in physics, and retained this place, at least with respect to its essential elements, even when the photon was discovered.

Other examples of explanatory theories are found in all experiential sciences. In physical science, for example, there is the atomic hypothesis devised by Dalton to explain various physical and chemical phenomena long before the existence of atoms had been experimentally established; likewise, the molecular hypothesis which van der Waals, Boltzmann and others took as the starting point of a theory for the explanation of a large complex of phenomena occurring in liquids and gases, long before the existence of molecules had been directly determined. After the discovery of atoms and molecules, endowed with the properties which according to their respective hypotheses they ought to have, these theories lost their hypothetical character, but retained their place in science as explanatory theories.

An important much-disputed hypothesis which may be counted among this group is the so-called evolutionary hypothesis. To explain the remarkable data of comparative morphology, paleontology, embryology, etc., many scientists start from the hypothesis that the species of plants and animals are interconnected by a process of progressive descendance and perhaps even have evolved from non-living matter. The evolutionary theory which is based upon this hypothesis has as its task to indicate more precisely how evolution could take place. According to the factors which are considered to stimulate evolution or lead it into a certain direction, the resulting evolutionary theory is, e.g., Darwinian or Lamarckian.

Theory and fundamental hypothesis are inseparable in explanatory theories. For instance, a hypothesis concerning the nature of light is accompanied by a corresponding theory of light; an atomic hypothesis by an atomic theory; an evolutionary hypothesis by an evolutionary theory; etc.

In *cultural sciences,* too, it is easy to find examples of explanatory hypotheses and theories. However, in these sciences it is more difficult to arrive at an indisputable verification; therefore, in them such theories will more often retain the character of provisional theories. To illustrate the difference in character between explanatory theories in the physical and cultural sciences, we may point to a few examples taken from the cultural sciences, especially history; for instance, the theories concerning the origin and development of the French Revolution, the War of Eighty Years and the American Revolution. In history, as is true to a greater or lesser extent of all cultural sciences, it is difficult to see the facts objectively. Consequently, the explanatory theories of history will often be colored by the mentality or world view of their inventor, even in essential points; e.g. more materialistic or Marxian, or more spiritualistic. Nevertheless, this difficulty does not take away from the fact that such theories are indispensable and will have to play a permanent role in the science in question. It should be clear also that, although such theories are explanatory in nature, they differ considerably in character and structure from the explanatory theories of physical science. Later we shall have an opportunity to return to this difference.

III. THE FORMULATION OF HYPOTHESES AND THEORIES

Regarding the formulation of theories in the ideal sciences, we may refer to the considerations offered above, in Section I, which will be dealt with again in the study of these sciences in the second volume of this work. At present, we will restrict ourselves to theories in the experiential sciences. Moreover, no special attention will be paid to provisional theories because, as a rule, these theories do not offer any special difficulties, and if there are any, no general rule for their solution can be given. In provisional theories much depends upon the scientific intuition of the scientist. Insofar as *provisional causal theories* are concerned, the problems generally are analogous to those of the explanatory theories which will be considered in this section. The construction of *phenomenological theories* does not offer any special difficulties. In them, there is no question of a hypothesis in the strict sense of the term, for these theories start from verified laws or principles and develop by deducing consequences from them. Hence we may limit ourselves to *explanatory theories*. Because these theories start from one or several hypotheses, we shall have to devote most of our attention to the formulation of hypotheses.

Again, it will be impossible to consider all the aspects of this question within the limited scope of this book. Only some important points will be considered. In the first place, we will pay attention to a few general difficulties encountered in the formulation of explanatory hypotheses in experiential sciences. Secondly, we will speak about analogy as an important aid in the formulation of hypotheses.

1. *General Difficulties in the Formulation of a Hypothesis*

A Suitable Starting Point. The first difficulty will be met in searching for a suitable starting point of the hypothesis. The hypothesis has to be concerned with reality and precisely with those elements of reality which, at the moment when the hypothesis is formulated, are not or at least not completely within the reach of immediate observation. For the purpose is to discover the mechanism or producing causes of something which is observable only in its activities or effects. Man, with his spiritual-material nature, who even in the most subtle constructions of his intellect remains dependent upon sense images, will have to try to form a suitable image or phantasm of that which has to be expressed in the hypothesis. It is possible that the phenomena themselves will offer a definite suggestion in this line. In other cases, as we will see more extensively in the next part of this chapter, there is a possibility that the analogy of the phenomena under investigation with other better known data will indicate a solution. However, it is not possible to give general directives for the technique of formulating hypotheses and theories. Here, again, much will depend upon the intuition of the man of research.

Inadequacy of Available Data. Because the formulation of an explanatory theory must be guided solely by the available data whose explanation is sought, serious difficulties are likely to arise. For example, it should be clear that a hypothesis and the theory built upon it can never be quite correct and complete if they do not cover all relevant data, whether the reason for the incompleteness be that all the data are not known or that some have been overlooked in the formulation of the theory. Thus, for instance, it was impossible to form a correct theory of thunderstorms before an adequate insight had been obtained into the complex and ever-changing structure and ionization of the atmosphere; or of the structure of atoms before there was sufficient knowledge of the phenomena of radioactivity, radiation and other similar things. Newly discovered phenomena will often make it necessary to revise the structure of a hypothesis and the theory built upon it. Something similar applies also to the cultural sciences; e.g. history and archeology. Here, too, a hypothesis and theory will be more correct and complete according as their inventor has had more data at his disposal.

In the progress of scientific research new data are gathered only step by step; hence it will frequently happen that no certainty can be had concerning the question whether or not all important data relevant to a definite object are known.   Moreover, in experiential science there are no *a priori* rules to determine which data are relevant.   Our insight into the relevancy of data increases according as continued research allows us to separate the important from the unimportant.   The fewer the data known, the greater the possibility that different competing explanatory hypotheses will be formulated.   In such a case, only the discovery of entirely new data will make a rational choice possible.   However, when no direct choice can be made between competing fundamental hypotheses, there will often be a possibility to make an indirect choice, as we shall see in the fourth section of this chapter.

2. *Hypothesis and Analogy*

Description.   In order to obtain the necessary pictures or images, the formulation of explanatory hypotheses often takes its guidance from the resemblance or analogy of the investigated phenomena with other phenomena which are better understood. Thus the better known is made to serve as an example or model in the formulation of the hypothesis and the development of the theory.

It may happen, first of all, that the phenomena under investigation appear to be perfectly similar to others whose causes are known.   From this similarity of effects the conclusion may be drawn that in all probability there is also a similarity of causes.[6] Thus, upon the basis of the spectral resemblance of sunlight to the absorption spectra produced in the laboratory, the correct hypothesis was formed that the dark lines in the sun spectrum must be caused by absorption in the atmosphere of the sun.   Such considerations, of course, always imply the conscious or unconscious presupposition of uniformity of nature (cf. Ch. VIII, Sect. V). The history of the physical sciences gives many other examples; e.g. the many models of the ether which were made analogously to mechanical models to serve as the foundation of hypotheses and theories concerning electric and magnetic phenomena, or Franklin's theory of lightning, which was based upon the analogy of lightning with an electric spark.

Very often, however, the resemblance between the unknown and the known will not be as clear as in the examples above.

---

[6]Cf. Chapter X, Sect. II, no. 2.

Nevertheless, even then it will often be possible to come to a hypothesis based upon one or the other observed or supposed resemblance. The best way to show how this is done will be through a few examples taken from physics, which offers the clearest illustration of this particular point.

Examples. As classical examples we may refer to the hypotheses which Newton and Huygens, relying upon analogies, formulated as foundations of their respective theories of light. Light is a phenomenon of propagation; hence there had to be something emitted and transmitted through a medium by the source of light. Known were, on the one hand, the phenomena of propulsion of projected missiles, and on the other, the propagation of waves in a liquid when its equilibrium is disturbed. Newton based his corpuscular hypothesis upon the analogy of light with the first model, while Huygens used the other for his wave theory.

Rutherford and Bohr made use of the known system of the sun and its planets as a model in their hypothesis concerning the structure of the atom. Louis de Broglie was guided in the formulation of his hypothesis regarding the wave theory of matter by considerations about a supposed analogy of matter and light. Light reveals a double character—on the one hand, it is undulatory; on the other, it is corpuscular, inasmuch as the energy and momentum of light corpuscles in a beam of light are directly related to the frequency and wave length of the corresponding light waves. Couldn't there be duality also in matter, couldn't there be in matter, alongside the corpuscular character of a beam of moving particles, a wave structure whose frequency and wave length would be deducible from the energy and momentum of the particles of matter? Upon this hypothesis de Broglie built his theory concerning the wave nature of matter. It was a daring but brilliant hypothesis, which the data of experience have subsequently verified.

De Broglie's theory induced Schrödinger to formulate his wave mechanics, in which he took his guidance from a supposed analogy with the twofold way in which the phenomena of light can be described—namely, according to geometrical optics or according to wave optics. Classical mechanics is analogous to geometrical optics. Schrödinger started from the hypothesis that, apart from the description of phenomena in accordance with classical mechanics, another description could be given according to a mechanics which is related to classical mechanics as wave optics is to geometrical optics. In this way, he arrived at the formulation of his wave mechanics, which works with wave equations. The operators occurring in these equations were chosen in such a way that the resolutions agreed with the data of experience.

These examples, which could be multiplied by many others, should be sufficient to show what was meant when the role was indicated which analogy and model may be able to play in the formulation of a hypothesis. Working out the analogy and analyzing the chosen model often throws light upon the phenomena under investigation. They stimulate further research and thus are able also to lead to new discoveries.

In cultural sciences the efforts to acquire more insight into phenomena in which man is a factor will be able to derive support from the resemblance of human nature in all men. Thus the man of research, who himself is human, will be able to form a more or less accurate picture of the motives or ideologies which are or were the basis of the investigated human activities. However, in this matter there is a grave danger of mistakes, especially with respect to the behavior of individuals, as is often the case in historical sciences. For the human mind is very complex and not easy to probe, and totally different motives or considerations may lead to the same results.

3. *Dangers of Inexpert Use of Analogy. Superfluous Elements in a Hypothesis*

In the formulation of an explanatory hypothesis with the aid of analogy difficulties are likely to occur. It has even happened repeatedly in the past that such difficulties led to deplorable results. The reason for these difficulties is as follows. The model which is taken as the starting point of analogous considerations will usually exhibit various aspects and qualities. Possibly only a few of these aspects have any importance with respect to the object investigated, while the others find no analogical counterpart in this object. In the case of a mechanical model, for instance, one can distinguish form, dimensions, velocities, forces, etc. If such a model is used in the formulation of a hypothesis, care has to be taken not to incorporate indiscriminately into the hypothesis all aspects of the model as constituent elements, but only those which are necessary for the explanation of the investigated phenomena. The others are completely superfluous and may even give rise to peculiar difficulties, as we shall see in Section IV, which is concerned with the verification of hypotheses and theories. Of course, it is not always very easy to see which elements are necessary or superfluous. Sometimes the question will become clear only later when there has been an increase of experiential data. Accordingly, it may happen that a theory will pass slowly through a process of purification till only the essential or relevant part of it remains.

Examples. As an example we may name Huygens' explanatory wave theory of light. In formulating it, he took as his model the known phenomena of waves occurring, for instance, in water. In laying the foundation for his theory of light, Huygens incorporated into it wave phenomena which were supposed to occur in a hypothetical medium, called ether. Transversal vibrations were assumed to take place in this medium analogous to the transversal motion of particles in liquid waves. However, for the explanation of the experimental data of light it was only necessary to assume wave phenomena to which a frequency, wave length, and velocity of propagation could be attributed and which possessed certain transversal characteristics. Of course, a kind of medium had to be admitted to make wave phenomena possible, but it was not necessary to assume the local vibration of particles which occurs in a solid or liquid. This element, the local vibration of particles, was superfluous and later led to such difficulties that some scientists finally rejected the whole theory of ether. This rejection, however, is not justifiable, for even now Huygens' theory at least so far as its essential elements are concerned, can be maintained as an explanatory theory.

Another example is the modern atomic theory formulated by Rutherford and Bohr. Here again, in the beginning too much guidance was sought from the mechanical planetary model which served as an analogon. Efforts were made to explain the radiation characteristics of the atoms by means of mechanical orbital movement of the electrons around the atomic nucleus. This orbital movement, however, appeared not to be necessary. Essential were only certain factors which in the planetary model could be interpreted as typical factors of mechanical motion, but appeared to have a different meaning in the atom.

Let us add an example of inexpert use of analogy in the realm of the cultural sciences, for which we may choose political science. Considerations are often made in which the State is compared to a living organism. Undoubtedly, there is an analogy inasmuch as in both the State and the organism there is collaboration of different parts for a common purpose. However, far too often it is forgotten that a living organism possesses an inner unity in which the parts have meaning only insofar as they contribute to the functioning and preservation of the whole, while, on the other hand, the component elements of the State (families and individuals) have their own existence and their own purpose independently of the State. With respect to his own human values, man has the primacy over the State and therefore, in this respect, is in no way subject to the State. The State is for the sake of the families and their members, to make it possible for them to attain their purpose, which is the perfection of man himself in all his human facets. Hence there is danger in carrying the equation of State and living organism too far. As a matter of fact, in certain views of the State it has led to totally wrong conclusions, giving primacy to the State and making men wholly subservient to it. Accordingly, the consequent application of the ideas suggested by this analogy leads to the absolutist view of the State.

IV. THE VERIFICATION OF HYPOTHESES AND THEORIES

1. *General Considerations*

As has been mentioned above, in Section I, in ideal sciences there can be no question of extrinsic verification, i.e. verification by means of the confrontation of a theory with something external to it. Hence we will be concerned here only with theories as they occur in the sciences of experience, which include the physical sciences as well as the sciences of man and cultural sciences. Most of our attention, however, will be directed towards theories of the physical sciences because in them the characteristic traits reveal themselves most clearly. Nevertheless, apart from minor changes due to the differences between physical sciences and the other sciences, the rules to be established will apply also to these other sciences, as will be illustrated by a few examples throughout this section.

Phenomenological Theories. The truth value of a phenomenological theory will depend upon that of its starting point. This starting point is obtained by means of scientific induction from the data of experience and laid down in the form of laws and principles. If these laws and principles have been established with sufficient certainty and therefore are trustworthy in their generalized form, the consequences deduced from them can be trusted. Moreover, the experimental verification of certain consequences may give additional support to our confidence in the theory and its foundation. With respect to these theories, therefore, there are no special problems.

Explanatory Theories. The verification of explanatory theories, however, offers certain problems. As will be recalled, an explanatory theory is based upon genuine hypotheses, i.e. statements concerning a supposed connection of phenomena or their presumable causes which are not subject to direct verification. From such hypotheses the explanatory theory, with or without the aid of other firmly established data, deduces consequences which are related to the hypothesis as the consequent is related to the antecedent in the conditional proposition: if A is, then B is. In this respect it is irrelevant whether the explanatory theory is provisional or intended to be permanent. Hence, according to the rules to be explained presently, the verification of the hypotheses will depend upon the verification of the consequences deduced from it. But once the fundamental hypotheses are verified, the theory itself which is based upon them is verified and, in appropriate cases, may be given a permanent place in the edifice of science.

Verification Rules. For the evaluation of the truth value of a hypothesis, only those conclusions are important which in one way or another are subject to verification. The extent to which the realization or non-realization of certain consequences is relevant to the validity of the hypothesis must be determined in accordance with the general laws of logic regarding the validity of conditional reasoning.[7] We will limit ourselves to indicate the rules concerning the connection of hypothesis and consequence which are immediately important for our problem. Moreover, the rules will be worded in accordance with the terminology used here, and we presuppose that the consequences have been deduced in a logically correct way from the hypotheses. These rules, then, are the following:

1. If the deduced consequence is not realized, the hypothesis is not correct or at least not correct in its entirety. We will call this the *first rule of verification.*

---

[7]These rules or laws may be found in any textbook of Logic; e.g. J. Th. Beysens, *Logica of Denkleer,* Leiden, 1923, pp. 203ff. or H. Grenier, *Thomistic Philosophy,* Charlottetown, 1948, vol. I, pp. 101ff.

2. If the deduced consequence is realized, the hypothesis may be correct. Certainty in this respect is had only if the hypothesis is the only one which can lead to the consequence. We will call this the *second rule of verification*.

Once a hypothesis is verified, conclusions may be drawn from it according to the following rules:

3. If a hypothesis is correct, i.e. in agreement with reality,[8] all deduced consequences must be realized.

4. If a hypothesis is not correct, it is not impossible that one or the other consequence deduced from it may still be correct (this will be the case if the consequence in question could have followed also from another hypothesis or from a true element contained in the incorrect hypothesis).

These rules should be clear without any further comment. But because especially the first two are important we will discuss them presently somewhat more in detail and illustrate them with a few examples. First of all, however, the remark must be made that the rules apply strictly only where there is a necessary connection between a hypothesis and the deduced consequence; in other words, where the consequence cannot not-be or be different. Such a connection will exist when there is question of a subject governed by deterministic laws, consequently, only in the physical sciences. In the sciences of man and cultural sciences, which consider objects in which man's intellect and free will play a typically human role, one must constantly keep in mind that so-called laws and rules do not have to be strictly valid, certainly not so far as individual cases are concerned. As a result, verification will offer special difficulties. Moreover, theories referring to events which happened only once, as is so often the case in history, generally are not strictly verifiable. Usually, they are capable only of acquiring a greater or lesser degree of probability with the aid of cumulative arguments.

A last remark. It is possible that many logical steps may have to intervene between hypothesis and consequence, so many even that their connection is understood only if one knows the whole structure of the theory or at least that part of the theory which has led to this consequence. For instance, no one who is not at home in Einstein's general theory of relativity will see the connection between the funda-

---

[8]What is meant by 'in agreement with reality' will be discussed in the last section of this chapter.

mental hypotheses of this theory and the deduction of a deviation of Mercury's movement around the Sun. The understanding of such a connection, especially in the physical sciences, often requires also an extensive knowledge of mathematics.

2. *First Rule of Verification*

Explanation. The first rule of verification is: if the consequence deduced from the hypothesis is not realized, the hypothesis is not correct or at least not correct in its entirety. Without further explanation, it should be clear that if B logically follows of necessity from the admission of A, then the fact that B is not realized implies that A is not correct.

In the case of a hypothesis which contains only one element, the non-occurrence of the consequence imposes the rejection of the whole hypothesis and also of the theory based upon this hypothesis. If, however, the hypothesis in question is a composite whole, containing more than one element, it will be necessary to examine from which of these elements (A_1, A_2, A_3, etc.) the non-realized consequence follows. For the non-occurrence of the consequence will force us to drop only the corresponding element of the hypothesis, but not the whole of it. This is an important point to remember. To disregard the composite nature of the hypothesis in question could lead to the unjustified rejection of the whole hypothesis or too great a part of it, while perhaps everything can be maintained with the exception of the one faulty element.

Example. As an example, we may point to the above-mentioned theory of light, as it was originally proposed by Huygens. One of the elements contained in this theory was the existence of an ether which is subject to mechanical vibrations. Later it was seen that such an ether was absurd; for on the one hand, it had to be harder than steel to allow vibrations with a frequency as high as those occurring in light, while, on the other, it had to be so rare that bodies could move through it without meeting any observable resistance. Observing this absurdity, scientists could have been satisfied with the rejection of such a mechanical ether, i.e. an ether subject to local vibrations, and have maintained an ether which is subject to periodic changes of condition or state. Many, however, incorrectly rejected the whole ether and thus abandoned too much of the contents of the original hypothesis.

Superfluous Elements and Modifications of Theory. The non-realization of certain consequences may not only lead to the discovery of superfluous elements in a theory, but also induce its inventors to modify or replace the parts of their theory which are implicated by the non-realized consequences. For instance, in the modern atomic theory the mechanical character of the atomic model has been more and more modified and replaced by an abstract structure using only certain typical factors that are merely analogous to the factors which characterize the mechanical model; e.g. orbital velocity and such like.

3. Second Rule of Verification

Explanation. The second rule of verification is: if the consequence is realized, the hypothesis may be correct. Certainty in this respect is had only if the hypothesis is the only one which can lead to this consequence.

The occurrence of any consequence deduced from a hypothesis gives a measure of probability to the hypothesis or at least to the elements of the hypothesis from which the consequence was deduced. The more numerous the realized consequences are, the greater the probability of the hypothesis, at least if these consequences are mutually independent. In such a case, the various data of experience are said to 'converge' upon this hypothesis. A foundation for it may be found in the logical principle of convergence or cumulative proof, which will be considered in our study of the probable argument (Ch. X, Sect. II, 3). As adapted to its use in the verification of hypotheses, this principle may be formulated as follows: If several mutually independent consequences can be deduced from a hypothesis and if these consequences are seen to be realized, then the hypothesis will have a high degree of probability and may even reach practical certainty. Even in this adaptation, the principle appears to be immediately clear. True, it is possible that from a false hypothesis a consequence be deduced which happens to occur in reality, but with respect to two mutually independent consequences such an occurrence is no longer probable, and in the case of three or four consequences it becomes practically an impossibility. Of course, care has to be taken to make sure that the various realized consequences really follow from the same elements of the hypothesis, and are mutually independent.

Example. A well-known example of such a convergence is supplied by the molecular hypothesis. By means of the theory based upon this hypothesis, it is possible to explain a number of mutually independent phenomena of experience, such as the various aspects of the Brownian movement, the internal friction of gases, the phenomenon of opalescence at the critical temperature, the deviation in behavior of very thin layers, etc. From all these data one can calculate also the value of Avogadro's number, i.e. the number of molecules in a mole or in a mass of substance numerically equal to its molecular weight. The same number follows also from various other phenomena which lie in a different field, such as electrolysis, phenomena of ionization, radioactivity, Millikan's proof, etc. Thus the molecular hypothesis was confirmed in such a superior way that even its most militant opponents, such as Ostwald, gradually had to give in. In more recent times, the existence of separate molecules has been demonstrated also in a more direct way. This one example should be sufficient. Anyone will be able to find others in his own branch of science.

Predictions. It will often be possible to deduce from a hypothesis consequences whose actual occurrence is not yet known and perhaps even is not yet observable for lack of proper means. In such a case, the term 'prediction' is sometimes used. There are many examples of it in the history of the experiential sciences. In modern physics, for instance, there were the predictions of the positive electron by Dirac and of the heavy electron (meson) by Yukawa. Subsequently, both kinds of particles were discovered. Such discoveries, of course, gave great strength to the confidence in the correctness of the theories in question.

4. *The Use of Verified Theories*

The two rules of verification, mentioned in No. 1, were followed by two other rules. A few remarks may be made concerning the first of these, which was formulated as follows: If a hypothesis is correct, i.e. in agreement with reality, all deduced consequences must be realized. This rule, whose meaning is sufficiently clear, has value for both theoretical and practical sciences as well as for the application of science to practical work.

In the theoretical or ontological sciences, a verified theory will have a permanent value for giving insight into the whole realm of phenomena to which it applies. Moreover, it will be possible to deduce new consequences from it which are trustworthy and may lead to new discoveries. In this way, such theories may reveal themselves endowed with extraordinary fertility.

In the practical or normative sciences, it will be possible to rely upon theories of the ontological sciences for the foundation of reliable rules which may serve as directives in the exercise of human activities. It will be sufficient to point to such sciences as electrotechnics, mechanical engineering, hydraulics, etc., which make use of verified physical theories; or pedagogy and psychiatry, which apply verified psychological theories.

Finally, in the daily exercise of his profession, the specialized craftsman or worker profits from the normative rules formulated by the practical sciences. These few remarks should suffice to show the importance of verified theories for both science and practical work.

V. THE TRUTH VALUE OF THEORIES IN THE SCIENCES OF EXPERIENCE

Although in general we try to keep away from epistemological problems in this book, nevertheless it may be useful to say something here concerning the truth value of theories because this point gives often rise to disputes and misunderstandings. In our study of theories in the ideal sciences we have already made a few remarks regarding their truth value; hence we may limit ourselves here to the theories of experiential sciences. In these sciences, the question of the truth value of theories has obtained a certain celebrity and even notoriety, especially in physical science. For this reason, most of our examples will refer to the physical sciences.

As the reader will have noticed, in the study of theories in the sciences of experience we have always taken the realistic standpoint, although it was not mentioned explicitly. This standpoint is taken, as it were, spontaneously and intuitively by everyone in daily life as well as in scientific research. However, as soon as there is philosophical reflection upon the human process of knowledge, opinions become widely divergent. Because it is beyond the scope of this work to study epistemological problems *ex professo,* we cannot consider the various views in any extensive way. Nevertheless, it seems useful to mention several views succinctly insofar as they refer to the value of theories in the sciences of experience. Important for our purpose are, apart from realism, which will be considered last, idealism and the various trends of positivism.

1. *The Idealistic View*

For the idealist, especially the Kantian, human knowledge is a subjective process in which the senses and intellect, on the occasion of external sense stimuli, produce the object itself of knowledge and thus largely determine the contents of the known. In virtue of innate 'mind forms', we are necessitated to arrange phenomena according to certain categories, such as unity and plurality, substance and accident, causality, etc. The reality of the phenomena is not the measure of our thought, but it is the intellect itself which is this measure. The order which we think to perceive and know is not the order of things in themselves, but the order which, in virtue of the innate structure of our mind, we put into the products of our knowing.

This view entails a definite standpoint with respect to scientific theories. For the defenders of this philosophy, a theory is nothing but a subjective arrangement of phenomena in us in accordance with innate mind laws; an explanatory theory is a theory which shows that the data of experience can be arranged according to the category of causality.

2. *The Positivistic View*

The term 'positivism' comprehends a large group of rather divergent philosophical views. Classical positivism was founded by Auguste Comte (1798-1857). According to him, after passing through the theological and philosophical stages, man will enter the positive stage (of which Comte considered himself the prophet), in which he will see himself freed from theological and metaphysical prejudices and apriorisms and will limit himself to observation and classification of phenomena according to the laws suggested by experience. It is not permissible and even meaningless to go beyond experience. Thus every hypothesis concerning that which lies beyond experience, as well as every search for true causes, is rejected as illegitimate. Such endeavors belong to the metaphysical stage of man, which, says Comte, is past. For Comte, science is not knowledge of causes, but merely a description of regularity in nature, of the 'how' of events in the universe. It should be clear that in this view explanatory theories are exiled without hope of recall; only descriptive or classifying theories are capable of finding grace.

Closely allied to this view and leading to the same results with respect to the value judgment of theories is the standpoint of the so-called energetists and thought economists. To the first group belonged principally physicists and chemists; e.g. Ostwald. Their ideal was a science without hypotheses ('*hypothesenfreie Wissenschaft*'), which by preference would use energy considerations that are always applicable and have no assumptions concerning the probable causes of phenomena. As their model they took the thermodynamic theory. As proponents of the second group we may name Mach, Poincaré and Duhem. In their view, the ordering and classification of phenomena in theories has no other value than that of making things easier for the man of science. The theory to be preferred is the one which is easiest or most 'thought economic'. Because of its thought economic character, the thermodynamic theory was held also by this group to be the ideal of a theory.

Finally, a brief remark concerning neo-positivism. According to this system, only that exists or is meaningful which, in principle, can be verified. The question regarding the value of a theory or the meaning of an 'explanation' is meaningless because no verifiable answer can be given. However, the neo-positivists admit hypotheses and theories provided that they are, at least in principle, verifiable by means of observation and experimentation.[9]

3. *The Realistic View*

Description. After the preceding fragmentary survey of deviating philosophical views, we must devote a few moments to the realistic standpoint with respect to the value of scientific theories. According to the realist, there is a world of real things, having real extension, real properties and real activities. Furthermore, the realist accepts that sense experience is capable of giving a reliable picture of this world, so that for every specific sense impression there is some corresponding scientific reality in the outer world. However, the knowledge of the senses is not formally the same as reality, but merely analogous to it. Although the contents of the sense image is primarily determined by the real outer world, it reveals itself to us in a form which is determined by the nature of our sense organs.

Something similar applies to our intellectual knowledge. Our concepts of real things are formed by means of abstraction from sense images, and in these concepts we intellectually know reality

---

[9]For a critique of the principle of verification, cf. P. Henry van Laer, *Philosophico-Scientific Problems,* Pittsburgh, 1953, Ch. III.

according to its specific structure.[10] Because our intellect depends for its knowledge of reality upon the senses, it is directly capable only of concepts of those things which are within the reach of the senses. Indirectly, however, the intellect is capable of having concepts also of non-extended, non-sensible, purely spiritual things. Moreover, in its consideration of reality our intellect depends upon the phantasms of the imagination; the phantasm, either as a whole or in its component parts, is an image of that which is perceived by the senses; hence our intellectual knowledge of reality will be analogous, at least with respect to those parts of reality whose inner structure is beyond the reach of the senses.

Application to Theories. From these considerations it will be clear that scientific theories which are properly founded upon experience give a trustworthy picture of reality. Descriptive and explanatory theories do so in their own way. Descriptive theories teach us the factual relationship existing between phenomena in their mutual connection and interdependence, and, in appropriate cases, the existence of a certain tendency or direction in the development of real things. They provide us with a certain amount of insight into the material, formal, and final causality existing in this real world. Explanatory theories, on the other hand, give us insight into the efficient causes which produce or maintain the observed phenomena and the inner mechanism of these phenomena. Hence both groups of theories possess a truth value.   In their own way, they make us know certain aspects of reality and thus give us a picture of reality. This picture, however, is not formally the same as this reality, but only analogously —there is similarity, but also dissimilarity. There are objective elements in theories, but also products of our thinking; there is enough objectivity to give a trustworthy description or explanation of reality, but also enough product of thought to make this description or explanation analogous. This applies, in the first place, to all theories, inasmuch as they make use of concepts that are not adequate with respect to reality. But in a special sense it applies to explanatory theories because these theories often have to resort to analogous models whose elements have not all been verified by experience and their hypothetical causes are not subject to direct observation. Because of its unavoidable analogous nature, our intellectual knowledge of reality is only an approximation of reality itself and there-

----

[10]Cf. *ibid.,* Ch. I.

fore must not be identified with it. One who keeps this analogous character in mind will not easily exaggerate the truth value of theories. Moreover, in this way it will be easier to overcome most of the objections of non-realistic philosophers (idealists and positivists) and to reply to their difficulties. In our view, the realistic standpoint of Aristotelian-Thomistic philosophy is also the only one which, philosophically speaking, is adequate. However, for this question we must refer the reader to *ex professo* studies of the epistemological problem.[11]

[11]Cf., for instance, F. Van Steenberghen, *Epistemology*, New York, 1949.

CHAPTER TEN

DEMONSTRATION IN SCIENCE

INTRODUCTION

The purpose of every genuine science is to obtain *true* and *certain* knowledge of its object. To reach this goal, two conditions must be fulfilled:

1) There must be true and certain knowledge of the starting point and the presuppositions of the science. We have spoken about this point in Chapter VI.

2) It must be possible to deduce new statements from certain statements concerning facts or other established truths. Such new knowledge is obtained by means of an intellectual argumentation or reasoning, which usually is called *demonstration* or proof.

In the present chapter we shall devote our attention mainly to demonstration in the sense of the derivation of a new truth from a known truth, and not to the foundation of first principles, which cannot be reduced to others but belong to the general presuppositions of science, such as the general metaphysical and epistemological principles, the basis of realism, the existence of free will in man, etc. (cf. Ch. VI). It is not possible, for instance, to give a strict demonstration of the principle of causality, the freedom of men's will or our own existence, for these truths cannot be deduced from others, but are seen as true by our intellect in a way that is strictly proper to them. Hence it would be unreasonable to demand a demonstration of the principle of causality or the freedom of the will if demonstration is taken in the usual above-indicated sense. However, if the term is taken in a less restricted sense, as is often the case, there is no objection against the use of the term with respect to speculations concerning these general presuppositions.

Division of this Chapter. When in a preceding chapter we studied scientific methods, we came across reasonings and argumentations which allow the making of deductions from definite data. We shall investigate here the demonstrative character of these scientific arguments and the conditions required for a scientific proof.

A demonstration must, if possible, give *certainty* concerning *truth.* It is not sufficient to know something which objectively is *true*, but we must also be subjectively *certain* of its truth.

A demonstration which satisfies the strictest demands is called a strict demonstration or apodictic proof. The strict demonstration will be considered in Section One of this chapter.

The term 'demonstration' is used also in a wider sense for any consideration which by adducing reasons and arguments make a statement more or less probable. Such a consideration is called a probable proof. It will be studied in Section Two.

We will, moreover, pay attention to other divisions and kinds of proofs which are important for the understanding of various types of demonstrations and their scientific nature. Thus in Section Three we will speak about the causal proof and the factual proof; in Section Four about *a priori*, *a posteriori* and *a simultaneo proofs;* and in Section Five about the *indirect proof.* The sixth and last section will be devoted to the value of *proofs from authority* in science.

I. THE STRICT DEMONSTRATION OR APODICTIC PROOF

As should be clear from the introduction, the strict demonstration may be defined as a logically correct argumentation from true and certain premises. It terminates in a demonstrated truth. In Aristotle's terminology, the strict demonstration is called the apodictic proof because the conclusion is 'shown' to be true (from the Greek *apodeiknumai: to show*).

A strict demonstration must fulfill the following conditions:

1. The premises must be *objectively true,* i.e. express a relation of subject and predicate which exists in reality. From false premises a true conclusion may follow accidentally, but it does not follow in virtue of the premises and there is no certainty that the conclusion is true.

2. The premises must be *certain.* This requirement refers to the subjective condition of our knowledge regarding the contents of the premises. Any defect of certainty concerning the premises will affect the whole argumentation based upon them. The conclusion cannot be more certain than the premises.

3. The conclusion must be deduced from the premises with strictly *logical consequence.* Hence the demonstration must be a

syllogism in accordance with the laws of logic. Only in this case will the conclusion have the same character of truth and certainty as the premises.

One of the premises must be an apodictic or necessary judgment, having a universal nature, while the other may be an assertory or factual statement.

1. *True and Certain Premises*

The following categories of judgment fall under the term 'true and certain premises':

a. General metaphysical and epistemological principles which are understood immediately by the intellect; for instance, the principles of identity, of contradiction, of causality, and intelligibility; also the principle "every being has of necessity the essential characteristics of its being". This principle may be considered as a special formula of the principle of identity (cf. Ch. IV). It is applicable to all things to which in one way or another an essence can be attributed; hence not only to natural objects and human artifacts, but also to Church and State or other human societies and mathematical entities.

b. General principles in the order of quantity which through formal abstraction are seen immediately in the data of experience; e.g. "the extended is divisible" or "the whole is greater than a part" and various mathematical axioms.

c. General judgments concerning nature which are deduced from the data of experience by means of scientific induction. However, certain restrictions are necessary here (cf. Ch. VIII).

d. General judgments concerning man and human behavior which are based upon our insight into man's nature and obtained by means of induction. Here, again, prudence is necessary because judgments concerning free human activities have only a moral necessity and allow exceptions (cf. Section II).

e. Religious truths if there is certainty concerning the Revealing Authority (cf. Section VI).

f. Theses which have been established by a previous deduction from true and certain premises. An apodictic proof does not have to be established immediately upon primary principles but only ultimately.

g. As true and certain premises may be considered also postulates which have been chosen rather arbitrarily as the starting point of a theoretical system, as in mathematics and logistics, provided that these postulates are not contradictory. If such premises are used, the qualification 'true and certain' does not belong to them by virtue of their contents or verification but only by 'assignation'.

h. Finally, the immediate and singular judgments of experience which are based upon a trustworthy sense experience. However, such assertory judgments may be used only in the minor premise of the apodictic proof.

2. *The Character of Necessity of the Apodictic Proof*

In an apodictic proof in the above-explained sense we have to do with premises which are objectively true, known to be true with certainty, and the conclusion is reached in accordance with the rules of logic. In such a case, the conclusion will express a connection which is necessary, i.e. it cannot not-be or be different, and its necessity is known to us. The ideal is to know the necessity not merely as actually existing but *as a necessity,* in the sense that we know why this connection must exist and cannot be different. Very frequently, however, it will not be possible to reach this ideal because we do not have the required insight; for instance, in conclusions which are based upon Revelation and many conclusions of physical science. A genuine insight into necessity exists only in the causal proof (cf. Section III).

It is obvious that the character of necessity of the conclusion is proportioned to that of the premises. The necessity, however, of the premises may be of different degrees. As we have seen in Chapter Four, a distinction must be made between absolute or *metaphysical* necessity and the *hypothetical* necessity which may occur in different orders, such as the mathematical, the physical, and the moral order. Hence the conclusion of the proof in question will enjoy a corresponding degree of necessity.

A special difficulty is encountered with respect to the so-called *moral* necessity, which is proper to judgments concerning a general human rule of acting (cf. Ch. IV, Section II, No. 3). Because such rules do not have an absolute validity, but always allow exceptions, the proofs based upon these rules will have no greater value than the probable arguments which we will presently consider. As we will see in the second volume, it is especially in the cultural sciences and the sciences of man that this difficulty arises.

II. THE PROBABLE ARGUMENT

1. *General Considerations*

The probable argument may be described as a logically correct argument whose conclusion does not attain to more than probability. In Aristotelian language, as opposed to the apodictic proof whose certainty is not subject to doubt, the probable argument is called the dialectic argument (from the Greek dialegomai: to dispute).

This argument, therefore, does not result in certainty or knowledge in the strict sense of the term because there is no complete insight. It succeeds only in giving a subjective sense of probability, a presumption or opinion, regarding the truth of the conclusion.

Since the probable argument, too, demands a strictly logical consequence or formally correct syllogism, the lack of certainty can spring only from the defective nature of the premises. Both, or at least one of the premises, are problematic or probable statements. Examples of such statements are:

a. Judgments concerning the general way of human behavior, i.e. judgments expressing a moral necessity;

b. Judgments concerning connections whose necessary character is not known to us, although in reality they are necessary, so that the judgments, as a matter of fact, express necessary or essential connections.

a. The first type of probable statement is often found in general judgments concerning the course of action men will take in a definite set of circumstances; e.g. in times of danger, war or certain economic conditions men will generally act in this or that definite way. It is obvious that such a judgment does not express any inner necessity, except the so-called moral necessity, mentioned above, and that its application to a particular group of men or individuals will always be dangerous (cf. Ch. IV, Sect. II, no. 3). This kind of uncertainty will often be met with in the sciences of man and the cultural sciences; e.g. history and economics.

b. The second type of probable judgment occurs frequently in the physical sciences. From observation there arises a definite impression that there is a necessary or essential connection between phenomena, although it is not yet possible to be certain in this respect. In physical science such a probable argument will usually be the first step on the road to certainty. The impression gives rise to a hypothesis concerning the true connection, foundation or causes of the phenomena under observation. The hypothesis is able to stimulate further, more convincing research, which may be able to give the final foundation of a demonstrative proof.

From the preceding considerations it should be clear that, although the probable argument does not lead to genuine knowledge, it has its place in science. It is the natural preparation for certain knowledge of causes or a sufficient foundation for human actions. The deficiency of our sense knowledge of reality and the limitations of our intellect do not allow us to reach immediately the highest degree of certainty.

2. *Proof from Analogy*

A special group of probable arguments is formed by the so-called proofs from analogy. By this term is meant an argumentation in which by virtue of the resemblance (analogy) between two phenomena or groups of phenomena certain characteristics of one are attributed to the other. Such an argumentation may be considered to be a process of reasoning in which the principle of analogy is one premise, while the other is formed by a judgment concerning the resemblance or analogy between the phenomena in question. Both deserve a brief consideration.

a. THE PRINCIPLE OF ANALOGY

In a general way, this principle may be formulated as follows: "Similar (analogous) phenomena have similar causes, properties or effects". More specialized formulas of the principle will be given below. The principle of analogy expresses an irrefutable truth provided that 1) its application is limited to deterministic phenomena, i.e. phenomena which by their very nature can work in only one way; 2) the similarity in question refers not merely to accidental qualities or relationships but is really essential. If both these conditions are fulfilled, one is justified in concluding from the analogy of observed phenomena to the similarity of other connected phenomena, such as their causes, effects or modes of operation. The probability of the conclusion will be directly proportioned to the extent and certainty of the observed resemblance.

The first of these two conditions is always fulfilled in the case of natural phenomena in which man's free will plays no role. The second condition, however, concerning the actual occurrence of analogy in essential points, will often give rise to many difficulties.

b. Analogy in Essential Points

The analogy upon which the reasoning process is based must refer to the essential points which are at stake in the argumentation. Generally, however, it is, first of all, by no means *a priori* clear which elements of a given situation are necessary and essential, and secondly, sense experience is not capable of leading immediately to a definite answer. As a matter of fact, the resemblance considered in the argument has to be established by experience; sense experience, however, is always limited to observable phenomena (qualities and reactions) and alone can never distinguish the essential from the accidental. A sense perceptible or superficial resemblance in form, quality or activity does not always have to point to a necessary or essential connection, but will often be the result of incidental factors or chance occurrences. If in a given case intellectual analysis is capable of distinguishing the essential from the accidental, then it will be possible to formulate an apodictic proof. Often this proof will be merely a factual proof, but if an insight into the reasons of the fact is attainable, it may also have the character of a causal proof. Usually, however, this insight will be lacking, especially in the first stages of scientific research, so that the second premise of the proof from analogy cannot be considered to attain to certainty. Accordingly, the whole reasoning process will be no more than a probable proof whose conclusion has a hypothetical character. Continued research may be able to confirm it, but may also modify or reject it. In this continued research, attention will have to be paid not only to the points of resemblance, but especially to dissimilarities and their influence upon the whole. For similar causes are capable of producing dissimilar effects if there is a variation of circumstances in which different co-causes exercise influence. Hence in many cases there will be merely an apparent analogy, so that the reasoning process in question will be a sophism. This sophism is called the fallacy of analogy.

c. Examples of the Use of Analogy in Science

The above-mentioned considerations about the use of analogy may be illustrated by a few applications in which the principle of analogy is formulated in various special ways.

Analogous Causes Have Analogous Effects or Actions. This principle is often applied, explicitly or implicitly, in the physical sciences of animate and inanimate nature, especially in comparative anatomy and physiology. The formula is often further adapted to the realm of its application; for instance, analogous organs have analogous functions. Although such principles must be used with the necessary prudence, they have shown their usefulness in biological sciences and especially in the study of the human body. While the human body in no respect is perfectly equal to that of animals but analogous to theirs, experiments on animals may provide valuable information when direct experiments on man are not possible.

Analogous Phenomena Have Analogous Causes. Guided by this principle, Franklin concluded from the similarity of lightning and electric sparks to analogy of their causes, i.e. to the presence of electric charges in the atmosphere whose discharge give rise to flashes of lightning. The principle is used also in animal psychology when from the analogy of reactions to similar stimuli or from analogous observations in man and animals one concludes to analogy of processes, sensations, or emotions with respect to man and animals. However, there is great danger in the application of this principle to the psychical life of animals because it is not possible to obtain reliable data concerning the existence or nature of an inner emotional life in animals and therefore impossible also to state to what extent there is true analogy. For instance, it certainly was a wrong application of analogy when upon the basis of the superficial resemblance the phenomena of life began to be considered as purely physico-chemical processes, or when certain ways of animal behavior were put on line with the tropisms of plants.

The Course of Analogous Phenomena Follows Analogous Laws. This expression differs in form from the preceding ones, but its contents is the same, for the observance of similar laws flows precisely from the relationship of cause and effect in deterministic phenomena. Nevertheless the formula has its practical use when the causal connection is not immediately clear or one wants to leave this connection out of consideration.

In physical science this principle is often followed intuitively; e.g. when from the resemblance between phenomena of sound, light and heat the conclusion is drawn that they must follow analogous courses with respect to, for instance, propagation, refraction, deflection and interference. In the realm of biological sciences there is an application which may be formulated as: equal external factors influence analogous organs or functions in an analogous way. This principle is used in medicine when, after experimenting with a treatment upon animals and observing its effect, the same is applied to man in the confident expectation that the physiological reactions will be analogous to those observed in animals.

Haeckel took this principle as his starting point in the formulation of his fundamental biogenetic law that the ontogenesis of the individual is a repetition of its phylogenesis, i.e. the origin of a species by way of evolution. From the various stages occurring in ontogenetic evolution a conclusion could be drawn, he thought, concerning the successive stages of development which would have led to the species present. However, it is not at all *a priori* clear that there is an analogy between ontogenesis and phylogenesis, so that even *a priori* Haeckel's law must be considered to be very doubtful. Moreover, it has been shown repeatedly that also as a matter of fact the biogenetic law has no value for the solution of the problem of evolution. Nevertheless the law continues to be accepted by numerous adherents of evolutionism.

Another wrong application of this principle of analogy occurs among certain sociologists. From a certain resemblance between a human society and a living organism they do not hesitate to draw conclusions concerning the inner order, growth and development which, they claim, must take place in a human society.

d. A Pari and A Fortiori Proofs

The degree of probability enjoyed by the conclusion in a proof from analogy increases in direct ratio to the degree of resemblance upon which the conclusion is based. The term *a pari* is used in reference to a conclusion when there is a practically perfect resemblance between the newly considered cases and others for which the conclusion is certainly valid. When such a resemblance occurs, the degree of probability reached with respect to the new cases or new group of phenomena is so great that it borders on certainty. To give a few examples, it will be possible to conclude *a pari* that the dark spectral lines of the sun and the stars originate in a similar way as the dark spectral lines produced by the absorption of light in the laboratory; in frequently occurring cases of a disease, the physician's diagnosis will have the value of an *a pari* conclusion.

By an *a fortiori* conclusion is meant that the reason which accounts for a certain result in one case is considered to be present even more strikingly in another case. For example, virtuous acts which are expected of every human being, *a fortiori* are expected of a Christian; if a healthy man can become the victim of an infection, *a fortiori* a sick person will be subject to it.

In this connection we may mention also the *a contrario* proof. This proof is an argumentation whose starting point lacks that element which is considered to be the foundation of the opposite conclusion. If, for instance, bad housing increases immorality, it is to be expected *a contrario* that improved housing conditions will have a favorable effect upon general morality.

Remarks. The reasoning process which above has been studied under the name 'proof from analogy' is sometimes called *analogous induction.* In our view, the use of this term is not to be recommended. In the proof from analogy it is not primarily a question of a transition from the particular to the universal, but, as is clear from the examples, rather a transition from one group to another group or from one individual to another individual which has certain similarities with the first.

It is true, of course, that, as we have seen in Ch. VII, Sect. I, no. 5, analogy is sometimes used to arrive, after an investigation of a number of individual instances, at a collectively general judgment which is considered to be valid for the observed cases as well as for non-observed but analogous instances. But even in this case the use of the term 'analogous induction' is not recommendable. Preferably, one should speak of by-analogy-completed induction.

3. Convergence

With respect to a scientific problem it may be possible to arrive at the same conclusion in different and mutually independent ways, each of which does not allow more than probability. In such a case, the conclusion will have a much greater degree of probability than could be attributed to it upon the basis of each argument taken separately. Occasionally, the conclusion may even reach the mark of certainty. The foundation for this greater probability or practical certainty lies in the so-called *principle of convergence,* which may be formulated as follows: If a number of mutually independent arguments which separately have only a probable value lead to the same conclusion, this conclusion will have a high degree of certainty and truth. The principle would seem to be clear enough and not to need any comment. Of course, a necessary condition for its validity is that the various arguments are really independent of one another, i.e. have different starting points. In general, when one starting point does not lead to more than a probable conclusion, efforts will be made to obtain the same result by starting from a different datum.

The method of convergence is used in all sciences. To give a few examples, in history converging proofs are used to show that a disputed person lived at a definite time or was responsible for definite events; in astronomy and geology convergence has led to a reliable estimate of the age of the universe and the earth. Moreover, as we have seen in the preceding chapter (Sect. IV, no. 3), the method of convergence is generally used in the verification of hypotheses.

III. THE CAUSAL AND FACTUAL PROOFS

In both the strict demonstration and the probable argument a distinction can be made between the causal and the factual proof. A *causal* proof (*demonstratio propter quid*) is a process of reasoning which shows a relation as arising of necessity from its causes. A *factual* proof (*demonstratio quia* or *quod*), also called an assertory proof, is an argumentation which reveals the actual existence of a relation without however giving any insight into the reason for the relation.

This division is nothing new. It may be found in Aristotle, who distinguished *'dióti'* and *'óti'* proofs.[1]

The division is adequate because it is based upon contradictory opposition—either there is an insight into the cause of the relation, and then the proof is causal, or there is no such insight, and then the proof is factual. Accordingly, every proof which is not a causal proof, will automatically have to be classified as a factual proof.

1. *The Causal Proof*

According to the definition given above, the causal proof is a proof which makes a relation known to us in its causes. It is the only strictly scientific proof, for this proof alone gives genuine knowledge in accordance with the ideal mentioned above, in Ch. I. no. 3, "intellectual knowledge with insight into the causes why a

---

[1]*Anal. Post.*, I, 13 (78a 22).

thing is". Only to this proof is it possible to apply in the strict sense the classical definition: "a syllogism which makes us know".

Requirements of the Causal Proof. To be causal in the strict sense of the term, a proof must satisfy several requirements with respect to the causes upon which it is based.

1. The causes in question must have a truly *ontological value,* i.e. they must determine the existence of the relationship and not merely be logical causes which make the relation known to us. An effect, for instance, or a property can be the logical cause of our knowledge of its real cause or subject, but in such a case that which is ontologically prior in being is logically posterior in being known.

The term 'cause' is used here for all causes of being and also for the so-called virtual or metaphysical causes. A *cause* of being is anything which by its influence determines the coming to be, the being, or the mode of being of something else. This concept implies therefore a real influence upon the being of a thing. In accordance with the various modes in which this influence can take place, philosophers speak of efficient and final, material and formal causes.

Apart from the causes of being, there are the *virtual* or *metaphysical causes* of a thing. This term is used for that which in the ontological order must of necessity be admitted in order to make something intelligible, although there is no question of a true ontological influence. For instance, God's immutability is the virtual cause of His eternity; the immateriality of the human soul is the virtual cause of its immortality; and the extension of matter is the virtual cause of its divisibility. Virtual causes are included under the term 'cause' when we speak of the requirements of the causal proof.

2. The causes must be known *as causes.* It is not sufficient to know that which actually is the cause, but it is necessary to know the cause as a cause, i.e. to have an insight into the working of the cause so that it is understood why the asserted relationship must be what it is and cannot be different.

3. In general, the cause adduced in the proof must be the *proper, immediate* and *adequate cause,* so that the effect in question is 'convertible' with the adduced cause.

By *proper cause* is meant the cause which itself in virtue of its own causal influence produces the effect. This requirement excludes:

a. Non-proper causes, such as circumstances, occasion or opportunity, which may have some importance with respect to the effect, but themselves do not produce it.

b. General or common causes; e.g. if man's mortality is given as the cause of death for this particular individual, or if a logical genus is given instead of the proper species.

By *immediate* or *proximate cause* is meant the cause which directly or without any intermediary produces the effect. This requirement excludes:

a. Any cause which is logically higher than the immediate class of being to which the effect belongs, such as the genus instead of the species. This case was excluded also by the term 'proper'.

b. Any cause which ontologically does not produce the effect immediately, but is separated from the effect by intermediary causal links. For instance, if a certain bacteria or virus is indicated as the cause of a certain disease, or if a certain disease is given as the cause of fever. Usually, however, this ontological distance is not considered to be an objection as long as the other requirements are fulfilled, especially that of 'convertibility', which we will consider in the next paragraphs.

By *adequate cause* is meant a cause which is neither too narrow nor too wide. This condition excludes any cause which is either more restricted or more extended than the effect.

a. The assigned cause is *too narrow* if it applies only to a part of the cases in which the effect in question occurs. For instance, if the equilateral nature of a triangle is given as the reason why in such a triangle the bisectors or the medians are concurrent, for the same is true of all triangles; or when man's mortality is proved from his composition of body and soul, for plants and animals also are mortal.

If too narrow a cause is assigned, the axiom "if the cause is posited, the effect is posited" will be valid, but not the reverse.

b. The assigned cause is *too wide* if it covers more than the true cause so that a further specification is needed to indicate the true cause. Without this specification, the effect could be different. Although the assigned reason is necessary, it is not sufficient. This mistake is made, for instance, when in explanation of the fact that the diagonals of a rhombus cross perpendicularly one gives the reason that this figure is a parallelogram; or when life is indicated as the reason of sensation in an animal, for, although life is necessary for sensation, it is not sufficient because plants also live but do not sense. In general, this condition is violated when the logical genus is given instead of the species.

If too wide a cause is assigned, it will be true that the effect demands the assigned cause, but not reversely that the assigned cause itself has this effect. However, a cause which is too wide may be used in a negative proof, in the sense that, if this cause is not present, then certainly this effect will not be present (cf. Section V, no. 5). For example, if a body is not living, it certainly cannot have sensation.

'Convertibility' of Cause and Effect. Convertibility may be considered as the criterion of the adequacy of a cause, i.e. the assigned cause must be connected with the effect in question in such a way that this effect demands the cause assigned and that this cause itself produces this effect. If a cause satisfies this criterion, it will be the proper cause. However, an ontological distance of cause and effect, as mentioned above, is not excluded.

2. *The Factual Proof*

According to the description given above, the factual proof is an argumentation which reveals the actual existence of a relationship, without however giving any actual insight into the reason for the relation. In such a proof knowledge arises from a logical cause which does not necessarily coincide with the ontological cause of the thing known. Several groups of actual proofs may be classified under this general description.

a. *Proofs Giving Certainty Concerning Actual Existence.* Such are, for instance, proofs for the actual occurrence of a historical event or the existence of a historical person, the actual existence of things in nature or the reality of a given relation. A proof of this type presupposes a certain amount of understanding of that whose existence one wants to prove. If, for example, in physics one wants to establish that there actually are mesons and neutrinos or an ether, one has to possess an idea of what is meant by these terms. However, profound knowledge or distinct ideas are not necessary. It is sufficient to have a clear idea, i.e. one which makes it possible to distinguish the object in question from others. Thus it will often be possible to derive from the nature of phenomena a vague kind of knowledge concerning the attributes which their supposed cause must have, and these attributes will be sufficient to distinguish the subject exercising this causality from all others. Once the existence of the cause is known, efforts can be made to arrive at a better knowledge of its nature and thus make its definition possible.

b. *Proofs From General or Remote Causes.* The reasons put forward in such a proof do not satisfy the required condition of the causal proof that the adduced causes be proper and immediate (cf. no. 1). Examples: to conclude to the death of this individual from the fact that man in general is mortal; or, if a certain disease is given as the cause of fever.

c. *Proofs From Effects or Properties.* These proofs are based upon the principle of causality or that of sufficient reason. For instance, to conclude from smoke to fire or from fever to sickness.

Many proofs which give certainty concerning actual existence will have to proceed from effects or properties. As an example one may point also to the proofs for the existence of God which conclude from the existence of a world to that of God. Although in this case the effect is not proportionate to the cause, nevertheless it is possible to conclude with certainty to the existence of an extramundane cause endowed with certain attributes.

d. *A Simultaneo Proofs.* These proofs establish the existence of of another thing which is connected with the first of necessity and simultaneously (cf. Sect. IV).

IV. A PRIORI, A POSTERIORI, A SIMULTANEO, AND CIRCULAR PROOFS

A proof is called *a priori, a posteriori* or *a simultaneo* according as the known datum which is the starting point is ontologically or in the order of being prior to, posterior to, or simultaneous with the unknown consequence.

The A Priori Proof. This proof reasons from what is ontologically prior to what is ontologically posterior. A reasoning process of this kind occurs when one argues from cause to effect, from essence to properties, or from species to individual. Thus it will be an *a priori* proof if one concludes from God's wisdom to the existence of order and finality in this world, or from the mathematical nature of a figure to its properties. The term '*a priori* proof' is used also in reference to the application of a law or thesis to a particular instance.

The *a priori* proof is used in procedures which follow the synthetic method, described above, in Chapter VII (Sect. II, no. 2).

The A Posteriori Proof. Proofs of this kind argue from what is ontologically posterior to what is ontologically prior, i.e. from effect to cause, from properties to essence, etc. This type of proof is used, for instance, when one deduces the nature of a disease from its symptoms; the existence of God from that of creatures; or the presence of man in a geological period from the discovery of tools in the geological strata formed during that period.

The *a posteriori* proof is used in scientific procedures which use the analytic method, described above, in Chapter VII (Sect. II, no. 1).

The A Simultaneo Proof. In this proof one concludes from the existence of one thing to that of another which is of necessity connected with the first, without either one being subordinated to the other as to its cause or ontological foundation. Both have a common foundation in something else; they are two sides or aspects of the same thing. For example, the right and left side of a symmetric object; the body structure and psychical disposition of man; the faculties of thinking and willing in a spiritual being; or the corpuscular and wave character of matter. With respect to the last example, it is possible to deduce from certain data concerning the wave character of matter conclusions regarding the qualities which refer to its corpuscular nature, and vice versa.

The *a priori* proof is more perfect than the *a posteriori* proof because it indicates the reason for the conclusion, although this reason is not always the immediate reason. In an *a priori* proof the premises are better known than the conclusion, not only with respect to man, but also in themselves, i.e. they express the innner intelligibility of the object in question. In an *a posteriori* proof, on the other hand, the premises are better known only with respect to man.

A priori proofs are predominant in philosophy and mathematics, while *a posteriori* proofs prevail in the sciences of experience.

The Circular Proof. A circular proof is a compound argument which successively proceeds *a posteriori* and *a priori*. In the first stage of this proof, one starts from a datum or effect which is more or less known and from it progresses to its cause, endeavoring to obtain a more profound knowledge of this cause through the use of auxiliary procedures. Next, one proceeds *a priori* from the cause which now is better known and tries to gain a better insight into the effect. For instance, from the order of the universe a conclusion is drawn concerning the existence of an extramundane Being endowed with an intellect. Then efforts are made to arrive, by means of other considerations, at a more profound understanding of this Being, and finally the better knowledge of the cause of the order is used to obtain a more perfect insight into this order itself.

Such a circular proof is not a vicious circle. A vicious circle arises when from A one concludes to B, and from B again to A, as for instance, Plato, without adding in either case any new arguments, 'proves' in the *Theaetetes* the spirituality of the soul from its immortality, and in the *Phaedo* the soul's immortality from its spirituality.

The circular proof is only apparently a circular reasoning process. The conclusion of the first stage is taken as the starting point of the final stage only after it has been rendered clearer and more secure by means of other reasons. As examples of correct circular proofs, the following may be considered. The immortality of the soul can be proved from its spirituality, and from this immortality, as established by means of other data, one may conclude to the soul's spirituality. The divine origin of the Church can be established from Scripture, used as a historical and human document, while starting from the Church, known by other means as a supernatural and infallible Institution, the divine origin of Scripture may be established.

Relation of this Division to that into Causal and Factual Proofs. An *a priori* proof is a causal proof if it starts from the proper and immediate cause, but a factual proof if it begins with a general or more remote cause. An *a posteriori* or *a simultaneo* proof, on the other hand, is always a factual proof.

The causal proof is always an *a priori* proof because its starting point is the ontological foundation of the conclusion. A factual proof, on the other hand, is an *a priori* proof if it proceeds from what is ontologically prior, such as (remote) causes, but an *a posteriori* proof if it starts from what is ontologically posterior, such as effects.

Purely logical causes, which are neither causes of being nor virtual causes, terminate always in *a posteriori* knowledge and therefore may be used only in factual proofs.

V. THE INDIRECT PROOF

A proof is *direct* if it immediately establishes the point to be proved. There is no need to discuss it here because all our preceding considerations referred to this kind of proof. The direct proof may be causal or factual, *a priori*, *a posteriori* or *a simultaneo*.

A proof is *indirect* if it immediately establishes something else than the point to be proved, but in such a way that this point follows from it. Several types of indirect proofs may be distinguished. The indirect proof usually is less perfect than the direct proof because, as a rule, it shows merely that the relationship must be as asserted, but not why it has to be so. In other words, it is only a factual proof. We say "as a rule", because there is one exception, which may be called the indirect proof in the narrow sense. This proof is an adequate causal proof, as we will see in the following paragraph.

1. *The Indirect Proof in the Narrow Sense*

By this term we mean a proof which does not immediately show the point to be established but something else which is equivalent to it. Mathematics provides examples of such a proof in its study of loci. For instance, one can show that no point outside the locus satisfies the required conditions by showing that every point which satisfies these conditions is situated on the locus. In this example the conclusion established is perfectly equivalent to what had to be established.

2. *The Proof by Exclusion*

The exclusion proof shows that all, except one, of the theoretical possibilities have to be rejected because they contradict other data. In schematic form this proof is as follows: Given is P. To be proved is A. Proof: *A priori* there are three possibilities, A, B, C. But if B is, P is not; if C is, P is not. Therefore A is.

Obviously, such an argument by exclusion has demonstrative value only if the enumeration of theoretical possibilities is complete. In other words, the major premise must be a complete disjunction. Hence it is necessary to have a clear insight into these possibilities. This kind of proof is often fruitful in mathematics, where such an insight usually exists, but other sciences also make use of it.

3. *The Proof by Reduction to Absurdity*

This proof, too, does not directly establish the assertion which is to be demonstrated, but proves that the denial of this assertion leads either to absurd consequences or to the contradiction of true and certain data, accepted axioms or postulates.

An example of the first alternative is provided by the proof of the freedom of will from the absurd consequences of determinism which would make the moral order impossible.

The second alternative may be schematized as follows. Given is A. To be proved is B. But to deny B leads to the denial of A. Therefore B is. Such proofs from absurdity are often used in mathematics; for instance, the corresponding angles on two parallel lines are equal, for the denial of their equality would contradict the accepted postulate of parallel lines.

Other sciences also make use of similar forms of argumentation. Thus, for example, some have thought it possible to conclude from the dimensions and proportions of Cheops' pyramid that the Egyptians at that time had already reached a very high level of mathematical knowledge. However, this conclusion has to be rejected because it contradicts other established data which point to a relatively low level of mathematics.

We may finish with the remark that the proof from absurdity may be reduced to the proof by exclusion because in practice it amounts to the exclusion of one of two contradictory alternatives.

4. *The Proof from Silence*

This form of argumentation, which is often used in historical sciences, endeavors to show that a disputed event did not take place or that an allegedly historic person or thing has never existed. In such an argument reference is made to historical sources which should have mentioned the disputed event if it did take place are silent concerning it, or that authors who must have been informed about the matter and should have mentioned it do not refer to the event, person or object. Hence the silence of these sources is considered to be an argument in favor of the non-existence or non-occurrence of the disputed point. Obviously, great prudence is necessary in arguments of this kind, which can never give more than a degree of probability.

As an example we may point to the disputes concerning the authenticity of the Holy Shroud of Turin. Many argue against it by pointing out that the Shroud is not mentioned before the end of the Crusades in the fourteenth century and that in preceding centuries not a single author speaks about it, even when he could reasonably be expected to do so.

5. *The Proofs Against Opponents*

Under the general term of 'indirect proofs' may be classified also relative proofs, which are proofs against opponents. In these proofs, one's proper assertion is not established, but arguments are adduced to show a) either that the view of opponents, whether real or imaginary, who deny what is asserted cannot at all be proved (*negative proof*); b) or that the premises of the opponents lead to consequences which they themselves do not want to accept (*proof 'ad hominem'*).

a. *The Negative Proof.* In the negative proof, one does not establish one's own assertion, but shows that there is not a single reasonable argument in favor of the view taken by the adversary and therefore no reason to deny one's own assertion.

Such a proof will be more efficacious if it can be shown that there would have to be a definite proof in case the opposite of the assertion is true and that this proof is lacking.

For example, the assertion that animals do not have an intellect cannot be proved directly from experience. Usually, it is impossible to prove from experience that something is wholly absent. However, it may be pointed out that the opposite view cannot be given any valid foundation and that in case animals had an intellect their behavior would have to manifest it. But as a matter of fact, animal behavior does not reveal any genuine intellect. Moreover, one can point to the absurd consequences following from the admission of an intellect in animals.

It is possible to use the proof from silence as a negative proof against opponents. Nevertheless, great care has to be taken lest the efficacy of the argument from silence be exaggerated.

b. *The Argument 'Ad Hominem'.* This argument has direct value only insofar as it induces the opponent to cease his attacks and thus indirectly increases the strength of one's own position.

In such an argument the starting point lies in the premises of the opponent—whether these premises be true, doubtful or false—and one shows that they lead to a conclusion which contradicts either the opponent's view or his way of acting.

A well-known example showing an opponent's contradiction of his own views is that against scepticism. If one cannot be certain of anything whatsoever, then it is impossible to be certain of the principle that everything is to be doubted. Thus the very foundation of scepticism collapses.

An example in which the opponent's own way of acting provides an argument is had when it is pointed out to a philosophical determinist that his own behavior constantly shows his own inner conviction that he freely determines his activity.

VI.   THE ARGUMENT FROM AUTHORITY

1. *General Considerations*

In the preceding sections we considered mainly argumentations which are based upon insight and therefore convincing for anyone who is able to acquire this insight.   However, it will not always be possible to possess such an insight with respect to the starting point of an argument, especially when this starting point contains data concerning an actual event or situation or expresses a truth which cannot be understood by the human intellect.   The last case occurs if a truth, revealed by God, concerning something which surpasses man's intellect serves as the starting point of a theological argument.   Accordingly, in such an argument reliance is placed upon God's authority.   In the first case, on the other hand, where actual events of the natural order are considered, one will have to rely upon the authority of men in all instances in which one cannot personally observe the facts, such as historic events of the past and also many facts and events pertaining to the physical sciences.   In a similar way, one will often be forced to accept scientific theses upon the authority of others, without having a personal insight, because no one is able to acquire all knowledge through personal research, whether it be for lack of time or of intellectual ability.

Accordingly, there is ample justification for a consideration of the value of arguments from authority in a book devoted to the philosophy of science.

Generally speaking, the use of arguments from authority is certainly not unreasonable and even perfectly rational, provided that certain requirements be met.   Let us consider these requirements.

2. *Requirements of the Argument from Authority*

For convenience sake we will call the one upon whose authority we must rely the *communicator,* and that which is accepted upon his authority the *communication.*   To accept upon authority is also called *to believe.*   In addition, we assume here that the original communication is made known to us without any intermediaries.   To be rational, reliance upon authority with respect to direct communications requires that the following conditions be fulfilled.

1. It must be certain that the communicator has made the communication in question. This communication may have been given directly to us orally or in writing or be contained in a written document.

2. It must be certain that the communicator possessed the necessary knowledge and insight and that he did not make a mistake.

3. It must be certain that the communicator did not intend to deceive, i.e. his trustworthiness must be definitely established.

4. It must be certain that the interpretation one gives to the communication agrees with the intention of the communicator.

a. *Truth Revealed by God.* With respect to truths revealed by God, the second and third condition are beyond discussion because they cannot not be fulfilled. But it remains to be proved that God has really made the communication in question and also that our interpretation of it is correct. The first condition is concerned with the proof of a historical event. It has to be established by historico-critical methods and touches also the problem of intermediaries who transmit the communication. The question of interpretation is a problem of exegesis. Because of the special difficulties involved in our lack of insight into such truths, an authentic exegesis will often be necessary. For the definitive determination of revealed truths and their authentic interpretation we are referred to the teaching authority of the Church which Christ has founded for this purpose.

b. *Communications of Man.* Any communication of man which is offered to us as to be accepted upon authority must satisfy the four requirements.

Regarding the *first requirement,* as a rule, there will be little difficulty if the communication in question is of a recent date. In the case of communications made in the distant past, there may be special difficulties, which have to be solved through a historical investigation.

With respect to the *second requirement,* a distinction is necessary. If there is question of the simple observation of a fact or event, it has to be certain that the communicator was capable of observing it. If, on the other hand, the matter concerned was a scientific statement, for which perhaps a long and complex experimental investigation was required or difficult theoretical speculations, then it must be definitely established that the communicator possessed the required intellectual capacities and other necessary means. In general, it will be possible to accept, without objection, communications if one is convinced that the communicator is an 'authority' with respect to the subject in question. Nevertheless, one must always take into account the possibility that human communicators are subject to errors because of insufficient keenness of sense powers or intellectual capacity and sometimes also because of influences coming from man's emotional life. Such influences often result in an unconscious one-sidedness of view and the overlooking of difficulties. In cultural sciences one's view of life or general philosophic position will often lead to an incorrect interpretation of the facts.

Concerning the *third requirement,* in general, it may be presupposed that there is no intention to deceive. Nevertheless, because of human frailty deliberate deception is a distinct possibility which cannot be wholly excluded. Historic cases of intentional fraud teach us to be on guard in this respect. It is possible, for instance, that a defender of a theory, especially in a polemic exchange of views, through vanity or in order not to admit error, will deliberately twist the facts to make them fit the theory. Incidents of this kind have occurred in the past. Accordingly, it is imperative to be on guard against it in discussions.

The danger of deliberate deception is especially great in the cultural sciences, specifically in history, in which so much depends upon the personal interpretation of the author. The last few decades have witnessed large-scale falsification of history in certain totalitarian States, where the ruling powers decided what youth had to be taught concerning history. Occasionally, even physical sciences have become the victims of this method.

With reference to the *fourth requirement,* often it will not be easy to satisfy it, especially if the communicator himself has not clearly stated his meaning. In such a case recourse must be had to other means, which, however, often do not allow more than a probable opinion. Here, too, there is great danger that the interpretation will be guided too much by one's personal views and desires, so that often much will simply be put into the communicator's mouth. Difficulties of interpretation will occur especially with great frequency in the realm of the cultural sciences. We will have an opportunity to revert to this point in our study of the objectivity of experiential sciences in the second volume.

3. *Communications Through Intermediaries*

If the communication has not been laid down in writing by the communicator himself or has not been directly spoken to us by him, we will be dependent upon intermediaries who received the communication and transmitted it to us either orally or in writing. Such intermediaries must satisfy certain requirements, which practically coincide with those of the communicator.

1. It must be certain that the intermediary transmits the communication upon the authority of the original communicator.

2. The intermediary does not need to have an insight into the communication, but it must be certain that he knows the original communication and that he did not err in transmitting it.

3. It must be certain that the intermediary did not deliberately falsify the communication.

4. The interpretation of the communication given by the intermediary is irrelevant unless it expresses the proper interpretation of the original communication.

These demands would seem to be clear enough without any further comment. If they are met, we do not rely upon the authority of the intermediary but upon that of the original communicator, i.e. in the case of divine Revelation transmitted through intermediaries, upon the authority of God; and in the case of human communications, that of man.

Regarding the case of divine Revelation, it will be necessary to show by historico-critical means that the above demands are met. In this case, these intermediaries will be mainly the authors of the New Testament. The required argumentation is usually set forth in that part of dogmatic theology which is called '*praeambula Fidei*'. It is beyond the scope of this work to enter into this question.

4. *Value of the Argument from Authority*

The so-called argument from authority is not a proof and as such does not result in an insight. As soon as in one way or another an insight is acquired, the truth in question will be accepted because of this insight and no longer upon authority.

With respect to divine Authority (Scripture and Tradition), the revealed communication in its right interpretation is true beyond doubt and absolutely certain; hence it is able to serve as the indisputable starting point of the supernatural science of theology. Divine Authority often is the only possible way to arrive at certainty in theological matters.

Regarding human authority, if the requirements are met, the communications in question will supply a valuable contribution to natural science—'natural' being taken here in opposition to 'supernatural'. In general, however, one may say that such communications do not have more authority than their original source. Hence the scientific authority of the communicator must always be taken into consideration.

Moreover, in difficult problems, such as those of philosophy, the possibility of error cannot be discounted, not even with respect to the most expert communicator. Accordingly, in human sciences the so-called argument from authority is the lowest and weakest of all because it lacks the strength of inner evidence. Nevertheless, it would be foolish to reject absolutely all authority and everything that has come down from the past through tradition, as was done by Francis Bacon and Descartes, and to accept only that which can be acquired through personal insight.

On the other hand, there are also cases on record in which authority has been too firmly adhered to and its utterances accepted without discrimination. Examples of such an unlimited reverence for authority were found among the Pythagorians, who wanted to cut short every discussion with a simple *"Ipse dixit"*, (the Master has said it); also among many Aristotelians, especially in the Middle Ages, who did not dare to accept anything which went against the view of Aristotle, "The Philosopher". The reproach of such a slavish following of Aristotle is often addressed to Albert the Great and Thomas Aquinas, but unjustly so. Both resist precisely the uncritical acceptance of Aristotle's sayings. "Aristotle is no God but a fallible man", said Albert. Thomas often quotes the opinions of Aristotle and other authoritive authors, both pagan and Christian, but he uses them only, after serious examination, as a confirmation or illustration of his own view. He is not influenced by misplaced reverence. "Harmony, which is an effect of charity, consists in a union of hearts and not of views".[2] He never considers authority as the criterion of scientific certainty.

---

[2]*Summa theol.*, II-IIae, q. 37, a.1.

Authoritive communications are quoted by him as the opinions of others and distinguished from true philosophical arguments.

As a general rule, it is good to make use of the results achieved by our great predecessors and to give them a respectful but also critical reception. In matters where we ourselves through our own research cannot arrive at certainty, the authority of others who are better qualified offers support and provides a basis for a probable opinion or even certainty if all required conditions are perfectly fulfilled.

In our own era of specialization, in which it has become impossible for one man to arrive at something even remotely resembling the personal mastery of all sciences, appeals to the authority of others are often made far too easily. Without any critique, adherence is frequently given to whatever may be found in encyclopedias, textbooks and popular scientific works. Moreover, there is a strong tendency to accept as true and certain all utterances of a great man of science, even when they refer to questions outside the realm of his specialization; e.g. when a capable physicist speaks about philosophy or religion. In this matter, it will be well to keep in mind the warning given by Husserl:

> When it is really physical science which speaks, we will gladly listen and as respectfully as juniors. But it is not always physical science which speaks when physicists speak, and certainly *not* when they speak about "Philosophy of Nature" and "The Scientific Theory of Knowledge".[3]

---

[3]*Ideen zu einer reinen Phaenomenologie und phaenomenologischen Philosophie,* Halle, 3rd ed., 1928, vol. I, p. 38; also *Husserliana,* vol. III, The Hague, 1950, p. 46.

INDEX OF SUBJECT MATTER

161